Nancy Hutchison 1985

Nancy Hutchison 1985

The Patchwork
LANDSCAPE
THE LIVING COUNTRYSIDE

A Reader's Digest selection

THE PATCHWORK LANDSCAPE

First edition Copyright © 1984
The Reader's Digest Association Limited, 25 Berkeley Square
London W1X 6AB

Copyright © 1984
Reader's Digest Association Far East Limited
Philippines Copyright 1984.
Reader's Digest Association Far East Ltd
Reprinted 1985

Originally published as a partwork,
The Living Countryside
Copyright © 1981, 1982, 1983, 1984
Eaglemoss Publications Ltd and Orbis Publishing Ltd

PRINTED IN GREAT BRITAIN

Front cover picture: A serene patchwork of fields and hedgerows
in Shropshire's Clun Valley.

The Patchwork
LANDSCAPE
THE LIVING COUNTRYSIDE

PUBLISHED BY THE READER'S DIGEST ASSOCIATION LIMITED
LONDON NEW YORK MONTREAL SYDNEY CAPE TOWN

Originally published in partwork form
by Eaglemoss Publications Limited and Orbis Publishing Limited

Consultant

Euan Dunn

Contributors

Contents

The Patchwork
LANDSCAPE

Introduction

The term 'patchwork landscape' may convey an idea of randomness, a mixed assemblage of woodland edge, scrub, hedgerow and open ground – but its character is quite distinct, its origins and development easily traceable. However diverse, it represents a broad habitat type endowed with a rich wildlife community.

There are two main elements in the creation of this mosaic which has come to dominate our countryside. First and foremost, man has played a key role in promoting the welfare of scrub by planting trees, hedgerows and copses as field boundaries to protect his livestock and crops from harsh weather. In so doing he has also provided valuable ribbons of grassy banks, ditches and roadsides which are havens for plants that once enjoyed a wider distribution.

Apart from this regular network, man-made and continuously managed, another element in the patchwork fabric derives from those wilder unkempt places where open ground is in the process of natural transformation into mature woodland. Here there is rapid and dramatic vegetative change – scrub that is a brief but, for wildlife, highly attractive transition zone. The thickets in this patchwork are at once refuge, routeway and food supply. Foxes and rabbits often choose such cover for their dens and warrens and predatory weasels thread effortlessly through the labyrinth, drawn by the promise of vole, mouse and rabbit prey in the undergrowth. A great variety of bird species prize the structural support for nest-building and relish the autumn feast of berries and fruits which scrub plants produce expressly to be eaten, while lush foliage caters for insects.

Left: The village of Fingest nestles among the attractive and gently rolling arable countryside of the Chilterns.

NATURE'S HIGHWAYS

As they travel in search of food, mates and shelter, animals follow their own 'highways' – the hedgerows, walls, fences and rivers that thread the countryside of Britain.

Much of the British landscape is made up of a patchwork of fields and field boundaries, occasionally interspersed with natural features such as woods, rivers and lakes. Wherever necessary the countryside has been partitioned in order to manage and farm it effectively. A close look reveals that it is also dissected by a wide variety of animal paths, ranging from a few inches wide (those made by small rodents such as mice, voles and shrews) to several feet in width (made by larger mammals such as badgers, deer and foxes).

These animal highways serve the same function as our roads and tracks in allowing animals to move easily from place to place.

However, animals have to choose their highways with some care since, unlike man, they are susceptible to predation. They must travel by the most sheltered routes available, although this may necessitate going further – around the edge of a field, for instance, rather than straight across it. Field boundaries offer some shelter and they are exploited as relatively safe highways by an abundance of wildlife. If you look carefully beside a hedge or wall, fence or river, you may see a small but well-trodden path running alongside it; furthermore, in a hedgerow you may see well-worn runs through the hedge where animals have crossed from one side to another.

Animal travel routes Natural highways are

Above: An English patchwork of fields, woods and hedges. Where the hedges, walls and fences form a continuous, countrywide network, animals are fairly safe in their travels. In places, however, they may have to venture across open land (fields or heathland), taking refuge and finding food in copses and woods where available.

Below: A radio-collared farm cat perched on a fence. Its movements are monitored as it patrols the boundaries of its territory.

ploited by animals for a variety of reasons. First and foremost, they offer a sheltered route for animals to travel from one point to other. Animals need to move about the countryside in search of the resources necessary for survival—and travel out in the open always a hazardous business; small animals are in danger from many different predators, while large ones often have man—and his vehicles—to fear.

Food is obviously an important resource; animals move along their highways in search of food, which they find en route or in adjacent land. Furthermore, nature's pathways frequently form territorial boundaries and animals travel along them in order to define and defend them. Scent marks (those of foxes and badgers, for example) are commonly used to delimit a territory and these have to be replenished at frequent intervals.

Movement in search of a new home is called dispersal and typically involves juvenile animals (young foxes and weasels, for instance) which have been expelled from their natal range at the end of summer, and are forced to travel until they find a vacant area in which to settle. Solitary species, such as hedgehogs and squirrels, will also travel long distances in search of a partner with whom they can mate.

Nest sites Field boundaries provide sheltered locations for nests. Numerous birds and small and large mammals build their nests in hedgerows, walls or banks for the food, shelter and easy access to other areas that they provide. Regular hedgerow-nesting birds include the robin, blackbird, chaffinch, dunnock, yellowhammer and whitethroat, but the birds most dependent on field boundaries for nesting are both our native species of partridge, the grey partridge and the imported red-legged partridge. They prefer hedgerows adjacent to woodland or farmland and so the number of partridges that breed successfully each year depends on the amount and type of field boundary available. These ground-nesting birds are highly susceptible to nest predation and choose a nest site in a well-protected spot with thick ground cover wherever possible. They also use the boundaries, together with adjacent farmland, as a food source, taking green leaves of grasses and cereals in addition to weed seeds and insects.

Small mammals, such as bank voles and field mice, build their nests in hedgebanks, within hedges or in wall crevices, while larger mammals, such as feral cats and foxes, have resting sites and permanent dens in hedgerows or walls along their regular patrols. The resting sites are used as temporary refuges for part of the night or during daylight hours. Such insects as bumble bees and wasps build their nests in hedgebanks, and numerous other insects lay their eggs on hedgerow plants, upon which the larvae subsequently feed. In all these cases the nests are positioned

Above: A family of hedgehogs on the move along a narrow, worn track. Hedgehogs are nocturnal, travelling by night along sheltered paths in search of insect and other invertebrate prey.

Right: A regularly used deer track winding through woodland. Such tracks, again, are made where there is shelter to be had.

Below: The dunnock is a typical hedgerow dweller, depending on the habitat both for shelter and food. It feeds on grass seeds, chickweed and plantain seeds which fall to the ground and are easily picked up from the bare earth at the hedge bottom. One pair will defend about 100m (330ft) of hedge.

Above: A common frog on its springtime travels. Frogs and toads hibernate in ditches and hedgebanks and may migrate several miles across country via ditches, streams and damp hedgerows in search of breeding ponds and mates. Newts also exploit damp hedgerows when they disperse across country, foraging among the leaf litter. The present wholesale drainage of ditches has the effect of isolating these animals from breeding ponds.

nearby copses or woods, but a blowfly greenbottle will only disperse up to 500 (1600ft or so) in search of a corpse on whi to lay its eggs.

Amphibians and reptiles make great use nature's highways. Reptiles, for instanc frequently hibernate in hedges, walls or ban and can often be seen sunning themselv on a south-facing bank soon after emergi in the spring and prior to dispersal. All thr species of lizard found in this country e the insects and spiders readily available field boundaries. The slow worm is parti ularly abundant in limestone country, livi in dry-stone walls or stony hedge bottom the sand lizard prefers sandy banks; and t common lizard can be found on woodla edges and in hedgebanks. Grass snakes a vipers also use nature's highways and hibe nate in small mammal burrows in fie boundaries.

in sheltered places with easy access to food either within the boundary itself or in adjacent land.

Dispersal routes Nature's highways are used as dispersal routes by a whole host of animals, but the overall distance travelled varies with the species. A dispersing juvenile fox travels up to 17km (10 miles) per night along field boundaries or paths in search of a vacant area in which to settle. By contrast, a young water vole dispersing along a river or stream only swims a few hundred metres each night in search of an uninhabited stretch of water. A young grey squirrel, on the other hand, may move anything between 300m (1000ft) and 8km (5 miles) along highways to

Territorial boundaries Once an animal h established itself in a territory in a previous uninhabited area, or after dispossessing previous owner, it must defend the territori boundaries against other intruders.

These boundaries frequently follow natur or man-made land features because they a more obvious and easier to define than a arbitrary area of open land. Birds, f instance, advertise their territories by singir from fence posts or hedgerow trees along th boundary. Badgers use field boundaries t

Mammal movements

Observation of brown rat (male) and juvenile tom-cat movements reveal how they utilise highways on a farm.
Brown rat: A home burrow; **B** movement in shelter of hedge; **C** rabbits—food; **D** arable crop seeds—food; **E** hedgerow—nuts, fruit, seeds; **F** boundary of range not crossed—other rats present; **G** rest site en route to farmyard; **H** grain stores etc—food; **I** return to homesite by safest route.
Cat: 1 sheltered sleeping site in shed; **2** prominent places—urine-marked; **3** milk put out by farmer; **4** resting site; **5** farm track - easy access to fields; **6** hedgerow near wood—source of nesting birds; **7** rabbit warren—food; **8** small mammal runs at base of wall; **9** sunning spot; **10** thick hedgerow with small mammals, birds; **11** fence look-out posts; **12** undergrowth sheltering small mammals; **13** pasture with small mammals feeding; **14** resting site in barnyard; **15** road verge—cat scavenges for road-killed animals; **16** resting site; **17** garden of house with female cat—potential mate; **18** dust-bins—food source; **19** feeding site.

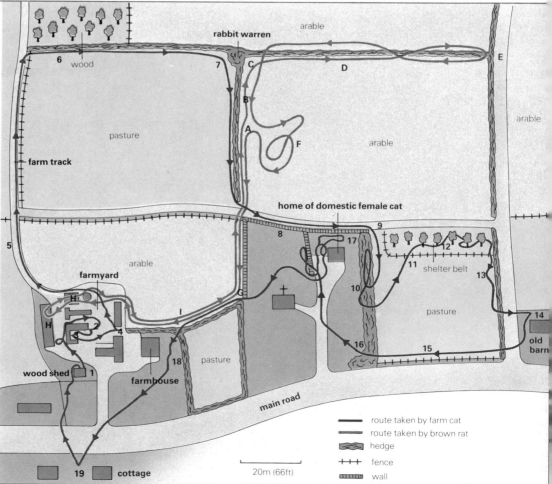

elimit their territories and mark them with
piles of faeces deposited in shallow scrapes
or pits called latrines. Members of a badger
clan regularly travel along these boundaries,
warding off intruders and depositing fresh
faeces in the latrines. Important latrines
situated in prime positions along the territory
borders are visited at least once a day during
the breeding season, whereas less important
sites are visited every few days.

Food sources Animals traverse their highways either specifically in search of food or
during some other activity, such as dispersal,
when they will take the opportunity to feed
as they travel. The highways themselves are
important sources of food, either directly by
animals feeding upon the associated plant
materials or indirectly by larger animals
feeding upon the smaller animals living
among them. Small rodents, for example,
sometimes live entirely within a hedgerow,
making their runs under the leaf litter and
foraging on the invertebrates they find there.

The larger the predator is, the greater the
length of field boundary it will patrol in
order to find sufficient prey. By radio-tracking feral cats it is possible to follow their
hunting excursions. A small radio transmitter
is attached to the animal and its movements
are monitored by picking up radio signals
with a special radio receiver and aerial. A
male cat may patrol an area of up to 80
hectares (200 acres) in rural farmland, while
a female will only hunt over 10-25ha (25-
60 acres). One young male followed on a
hunting trip concentrated at least 80% of his
activities along field boundaries, moving
several kilometres in total but often spending
long periods sitting and watching a rodent
burrow, waiting for the animal to emerge.

By contrast, a radio-tracked hunting fox
travelled about 12km (7½ miles) in a single
night along hedgerows and other field boundaries, catching small rodents and birds,
taking fruit and berries as it came across
them, and foraging for earthworms in nearby
pastures.

Weasels and stoats also concentrate their
hunting along field boundaries. Weasels
favour dry-stone walls, which they scour for
the small rodents living in the crevices,
whereas stoats hunt the same prey in their
runs among leaf litter and under vegetation.
A male stoat travels about 600m (2000ft)
during one hunting trip. Brown rats move
comparable distances along hedgerows when
food is fairly abundant.

The future Very little is known about the
overall effect of removing traditional field
boundaries, but it obviously eliminates the
resident plant and animal communities. For
the mammals the impact is unlikely to be
catastrophic: few species are confined to
field boundaries and the majority can live in
alternative habitats. Similarly, many birds
prefer a woodland environment but, if no
woods are available, they can exploit the

field boundary system of hedgerows.

Widespread removal of field boundaries
results in isolated patches of habitat with
no connecting highways and therefore no
connecting immigration or emigration routes.
Animals which disperse along field boundaries to new areas would be forced either to
stay in their natal ranges or to take greater
risks in attempting to disperse across open
land. Many animals would be confined to
small patches of suitable habitat, unable to
colonize new areas, and potential food
sources, shelter belts and nest sites would also
decrease. Species diversity would therefore
decline, and our countryside would be the
poorer.

Above: A honey bee on the
wing – it is visiting the
willowherb for nectar and
pollen. Such insects do not
travel as far as the birds,
mammals, amphibians and
reptiles but they, too, use
the shelter provided by
hedges, banks and walls for
nesting, and find food in
the plants growing there.

Below: A weasel alert for
signs of prey in the shelter
of an old wall. Weasels
hunt along dry-stone walls
for the small rodents living
in the crevices.

HEDGES: THEIR PAST, PRESENT AND FUTURE

Britain's landscape has been extensively reshaped to accommodate changing farming methods—most noticeably, perhaps, by the creation of hedges in the 16th and 17th centuries to enclose fields, and now, in the 20th century, by the wholesale removal of these hedges to make huge fields suitable for large machinery.

Below: In the eastern counties of England many thousands of hedges abounding in wildlife have been cut down to make larger fields—which are more economical to farm. This view of arable and pasture land neatly divided by hedges is from near Exmoor in Devon, where hedges have generally escaped destruction.

edgerows are a prominent and distinctive
ature of the British landscape, particularly
the lowlands. The oldest hedges are
robably remnants of the continuous wood-
nd that once covered most of Britain. As
llagers and landowners cleared the forest
or agriculture, they would leave the last
w feet of forest standing to mark the outer
oundaries of their domains. Today, some
f our most ancient hedges are the remnants
f such boundaries perhaps even now mark-
ng a parish border. Hedges were also formed
o enclose patches of land to contain domestic
nimals. This would have been done close to
he buildings of farm or village, and in many
laces these small, irregular enclosures can
e seen today. They indicate old field patterns
nd ancient hedgerow.

Creating hedges For many centuries crops
ere grown in large, open fields which were
ivided into small strips. Each of these
trips was tilled separately in an 'open-plan',
ommunal style of farming. There was no
eed to fence off the arable land and divide
into sections with hedges. Gradually,
owever, the old system changed, patches of
nd being enclosed and assigned to individu-
ls. The main period of enclosure was the
entury between 1750 and 1850, during which
arliament passed a series of acts empowering
andowners to add to their estates large areas
f what had previously been common land.
Rapid carving-up of the landscape, under
he supervision of government officials,
neant that patterns of straight hedges devel-
ped, forming regular, rectangular fields.
Wire fences were unknown, and wooden
nes were expensive, difficult to make and
equired frequent repair and maintenance. A
lanted hedge was a self-renewing, cheap and
ffective way of dividing up the open country-
ide into private compartments.

Changed farming The fields enclosed by
hese old hedgerows were of sizes appropriate
o the farming procedures of past centuries.
Modern ways of farming the land operate
ccording to a different set of 'rules'. What
vas a convenient sized field to plough with a
horse is now an inconveniently small patch
n which to manoeuvre a large tractor
hat can pull a plough along several furrows
t once. The hedges have become a nuisance,
necessitating more time-consuming turns
with the tractor and, of course, 'wasting' the
space on which the hedge itself grows.

The result is that the landscape has under-
gone extensive reshaping to accommodate
modern farming procedures, the main alter-
ation being large-scale hedgerow removal.
In the early 1950s there may have been over
563,300km (350,000 miles) of hedgerow in
Britain, but during the last 30 years the
length of hedgerow has sharply declined in
many parts of the country, especially East
Anglia. In counties such as Devon, where
arable farming has not expanded so rapidly,
the traditional kind of farming, based on

stock rearing, persists and so does the extensive network of hedgerows associated with it.

Hedge maintenance The top illustration
(see right) shows a common method of
creating a hedge or repairing gaps in an old
one. First, young shrubs are planted close
together. After a few years the stem of each
is partially cut through and the whole plant
bent to one side and woven between a row of
stakes driven into the ground. This forms an
effective barrier, and regular trimming keeps
the bushes dense.

The A-shaped hedge shown in the middle
illustration provides a good wind-break for
the farmer, is less liable to be damaged by a
heavy fall of snow, and is easy to trim mech-
anically. The tapered shape allows saplings
to grow into trees and so there is more
shelter for wildlife, while nesting birds, small
mammals and insects find good cover in its
dense branches.

When a hedge is just cut straight across
the top and sides, as in the third example,
saplings are not given a chance to grow into
trees, and the hedge tends to thin out at the
base, leaving less cover for wildlife.

Natural sanctuary For the naturalist, the
loss of hedgerows means loss of wildlife
diversity and the creation of a more uniform
and monotonous habitat.

Hedges are an important refuge for wildlife in otherwise open, inhospitable arable
fields. Hedgehogs are often found in a

Here is all that remains of a
hedge after destruction by
flail mower. The farmer
needs to cut down only a
kilometre ($\frac{5}{8}$ mile) of hedge
to extend his arable land by
almost half an acre.

Hedge maintenance

cut and layered hedge

tapered hedge

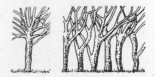

rectangular hedge

hedge bottom, and the mole has responded to the enlargement of field sizes by establishing itself under hedges, from whence it makes its forays into the open. Voles, field mice and shrews, including the pygmy shrew, are safely protected in the hedge undergrowth and for the insect-eating species – hedgehogs, shrews and moles – the hedge contains abundant prey.

Hedges are also 'wildlife highways', allowing plants and animals to disperse from one area to another.

History of a hedge The older a hedge is, the more shrub species it is likely to comprise, having had more time to accumulate additional plants. Indeed, the age of hedgerows can be estimated from the average number of shrub species found in a 30m (100ft) stretch of hedgerow. The newest hedgerows usually contain hawthorn, the species favoured for rapid hedge planting in the 18th and 19th centuries because it grew fast and quickly formed a dense, thorny barrier. For every additional shrub species found, one can estimate that the hedge is probably a further 100 years old.

Hedgerows also harbour large numbers of fine trees, particularly elms and oaks, which become a feature of the landscape and also home for many species of birds and insects.

Predators and pests The farmer needs to produce crops as efficiently as he can, but there is possibly a risk that by removing

Above: Hedgerow wild flowers – purple loosestrife, meadowsweet and mint.

Opposite page: A spring hedgerow in Devon.

Below: Untended hedges like this attract birds and insects.

hedges he could incur losses which ma outweigh the gains. For example, the hed; may be an important base from whic predatory beetles make their raids on aphic that cause so much damage to beans an many other crops. The birds of the hedgero include corn and reed bunting, whitethroa yellowhammer, song thrush, blackbird an linnet. The lesser whitethroat is most close associated with hedges – hardly ever is i nest found anywhere else. The insect-eatir habits of the hedge birds help to reduce th numbers of insect pests.

On the other hand, hedges also shelte many farm pests, notably rabbits, which mak raids into the fields. The farmer may prefe not to weigh up the pros and cons of pes and their predators, but hope to do away wit both together – by removing the hedge an treating the land with pesticides.

Wind barriers One beneficial role playe by the hedgerows is to modify the climat around them. They act as barriers to the wind When they are removed the wind can blov without hindrance in any direction ove enormous areas. In dry winter weather thi presents the farmer with the serious threa of drying out his ploughed fields, which can b harmful in the extreme. The crops have no yet grown much, so their roots do not bin the soil, nor do their leaves protect it. Th wind whips up the surface layers, includin seeds and costly fertilizer, and all this literall disappears over the horizon in a cloud c dust. The presence of hedges does not preven this altogether: a hedgerow only shelters downwind area equivalent to 20 times its ow height; but as a whole, a succession of hedge will combine to slow the wind and ameliorat its effects. Thus, by sheltering fields and wild life, they make their contribution to th countryside.

THE HEDGEROW AT HARVEST TIME

As the summer begins to turn to autumn, the plants in our hedgerows change in colour and a plentiful store of fruits ripens for both the residents and the visitors. The plants will soon die back, so the animals must prepare for the bleak months ahead.

An early hint of the change of season given when the first autumn tints appear. The food-making work of the leaves is now near done, and the green chlorophyll is beginning to break down, revealing other pigments which have, until now, been masked. In some trees the green colour begins to fade from the edges of the leaves; in others the change begins in the leaf veins. In oak the pattern is less predictable, brown patches appearing at random over the leaf surface. Inside the joint where each leaf is connected to the stem, a thin layer of cork forms: this seals the veins, and sooner or later the leaf falls.

Autumn decay In the autumn hedgerow the

ght: When fruits ripen, the g-tailed field mouse lects a store of berries, ws and nuts, which it en keeps in an abandoned st. It will return from time time in the coming nths to feed here.

low: An example of the re luxuriant type of dgerow. In autumn, the nite heads of clematis seed d the plentiful hawthorn rries provide an immense rvest for wildlife.

process does not stop there. The nutrients that the hedgerow plants have taken from the soil to build up complex substances will now be broken down and returned to the soil. This ensures that they will once again be available for the plants to utilise next spring.

Decomposition takes place in a variety of ways. Some plants and many fungi actually live on dead and decaying matter (including other plants): these are called saprophytes and play an important part in the breakdown of plant material. Many of the decomposing agents are invisible to the naked eye – the teeming millions of bacteria, for example. Others, such as some of the fungi including moulds, are more readily seen. White threads abound in the leaf litter: these are the spreading branches (hyphae) of fungi. Many species of fungi never appear above ground level, but remain in this thread-like form. Only some are able to put up the fruiting bodies that we know as mushrooms and toadstools.

Gathering the harvest Although growth in the hedgerow is slowly coming to a halt, it is by no means a deserted place. Man and beast come for their spoils, searching out the fruits and berries which are the end product of the plant growth of previous months. For country folk the hedgerow was important in the past. It was a veritable treasure house: a source of food, drink, medicine, shelter, fuel and dyes.

So many hedgerow plants satisfied man's needs that numerous superstitions have arisen. Of the hedgerow fruits, blackberries are particularly sought after by people and animals alike. According to tradition, however, it is unsafe to gather them after Michaelmas for that is the time the devil, as he was being kicked out of heaven, spat on the blackberry bush in his rage!

Today we collect blackberries by the basketful for pies, jams, jellies and wine: animals take them too, attracted by their sweetness. Wasps will be out on their final desperate hunt for food before the cold and damp kills them. Strong mandibles tear away the tough outer skin, exposing the juicy flesh underneath. This is an open invitation to many other invertebrates to take their fill. Various species of vinegar fly will eat from the damaged fruit; they share their harvest with bluebottles, greenbottles and drone flies. Red admiral and speckled wood butterflies can sometimes be seen taking the blackberry juice.

Other insects come for different reasons. The eggs laid by various insects in the bramble flower heads will now have hatched, providing hosts for the parasitic ichneumon wasps. The female ichneumon lays her eggs inside the bodies of the larvae. These eventually hatch, and the unfortunate hosts are literally eaten alive.

Fallen blackberries provide rich pickings for many mammal species. The bank vole and wood mouse take their share, and the badger also finds time on his nightly patrols to savour them. Dispersal of the seeds by these mammals and by birds is a way of ensuring that new plants will grow in other areas.

By mid-autumn the blackberries have lost their appeal, but are still attacked by moulds, which further assist in the decay process.

The white may blossoms of the hawthorn have given way to red berries (haws) which are succulent and nutritious to birds, including those winter visiting members of the thrush family, the redwings and fieldfares.

Insects visiting the hedge for autumn fruits provide a meal for the opportunist spiders. Webs may look empty, but somewhere a spider waits for its prey. Those created by the orb web or garden spider are numerous and especially attractive. Other spiders produce hammock-like constructions beneath them for their prey. As an insect lands, the spider bursts into action, pouncing on its prey. All species use the same tactics for dealing with the prisoner. The fangs inject deadly poison into its body. Sometimes the prey may be eaten immediately; sometimes it may be wrapped in silken threads and stored away, to be devoured later.

Mammal beneficiaries The autumn hedgerow harvest attracts small mammals: they collect more than they need, storing the excess for less prosperous times. The long-tailed field mouse, an inhabitant of the hedgerow normally resident in secret homes in the dense hedge bottom, takes a variety of nuts and berries, including hawthorn, wild rose, rowan and hazel. There is usually a plentiful supply of these in the hedge bottom, having been accidentally dropped by other hedgerow foragers. Should the need arise, however, the mice will climb up into the hedge to bite through stems holding berries. They may stay there to eat, perhaps using a disused bird's nest as a table, and many an unoccupied blackbird or thrush nest bears witness to their autumnal feasts. At the bottom of the nest lies a debris formed of the shells of hazel nuts, nibbled acorns, empty seed cases and the flesh of haws, often marked with stains from elderberries.

Quarrelsome and noisy shrews make regular patrols. Small and constantly active, they need a continuous supply of food if they are to survive. The shrews maintain their patrols even when conditions become less favourable, and many of them die in severe weather. Since they and other mammals are abroad, their predators – the stoats, weasels and owls – are on their rounds too.

Preparing for winter Among the mammals of the hedgerow is the hedgehog, which will be making its own arrangements for the coming months. Having selected a suitable site for its winter home, the hedgehog prepares the spot before retiring. Its nightly excursions become shorter and less frequent until it finally succumbs to sleep.

The squirrel, although perhaps less active for short spells, will be out and about during the autumn, preparing the many secret food stores which, in the winter, it will search out for sustenance.

Snails, which during the other months of the year have periodically sheltered in the hedge, now turn to it for a more permanent protection, as winter for them is a long inactive period. Sealing the mouth of their shell with a chalky plate (epiphragm), the snails find a resting place in the hedge bottom. Innumerable pupae of invertebrates, for example butterflies and moths, are suspended from the seemingly lifeless twigs, or hidden among the leaf litter at the base of the hedge.

Plants in autumn Between five and six

hundred plant species have been recorded in hedgerows, but it is unlikely that more than half of these will be found regularly. If by the end of autumn the small plants have almost all died back to the ground, this is only a resting period. Beneath the soil seeds lie dormant, ready to spring to life when conditions are more favourable. Climbers, including bittersweet (woody nightshade), honeysuckle and white and black bryony, become conspicuous at this time of the year. Earlier they formed part of the dense jungle. But now their coloured fruits, containing seeds from which next year's plants will grow, advertise their presence by standing out against the withering vegetation.

Above: The hedgerow is spectacular on dew-laden October mornings when the webs of orb spiders glisten the early light.

Right: The hedgehog finds shelter within a hedgerow a winter approaches and it is time to hibernate.

Below: Bank voles are among the commonest hedgerow animals. They are mainly vegetarian in diet, bu also live on insects, larvae and a variety of other small animals.

THE HEDGEROW— A WINTER REFUGE

Although the land looks bleak and empty in winter, there is constant activity in the thorny hedgerow thickets. Stoats and foxes use the sheltered passageways to stalk prey; ladybirds and earwigs crawl into hollow stems for warmth and protection; and birds fly from as far as Scandinavia to feed on the berries.

The hedgerow is a particularly rich habitat because it has characteristics belonging to two other habitats—woodland and open field —attracting animals and plants from each, as well as containing its own particular species. It offers a haven to all sorts of wildlife, especially in winter when the surrounding landscape is bare and exposed.

Hedge structure At the heart of an old hedgerow lies a dense shrub layer, often a mixture of hawthorn, blackthorn, elder and dogwood. At intervals along this strip, trees such as elms, oaks and ash create a broken canopy (before the days of Dutch Elm disease about half of England's hardwood timber grew in hedgerows). These trees act as host to all kinds of woodland creatures.

At ground level, a herbaceous border hugs the hedgebank along the edge of fields. This is made up of a mixture of well-known countryside plants such as nettles, jack-by-the-hedge and lords-and-ladies. These three layers— tree, shrub and field edge—are not distinct, however, for swags of honeysuckle, wild hops, clematis, bryony, bramble and dog rose climb riotously between them, knotting the whole together.

Winter shelter Hedgerows, especially of hawthorn with its tangle of spiny twigs, were planted primarily to contain livestock, and incidentally to offer them some shelter from bad weather. In this second role, wildlife also benefits, particularly in winter. Many birds roost in hedges overnight and a small hawthorn thicket may accommodate several hundred starlings and lesser numbers of fieldfares, wood pigeons, stock doves and magpies. A dense hedge offers them protection from ground predators and also from wind which causes greatest loss of heat (and energy) during long winter nights. With the onset of winter, many insects also seek nooks and crannies in the interior of the hedge to hibernate.

Hedgerow highways Hedges act as convenient corridors, making it easy for both plants and animals to spread in safety from one habitat to another. This can be essential for the survival of a species. If, for example, a particular insect is confined to one isolated woodland, and that wood is destroyed by fire, the species would become extinct. If the wood is linked by a hedgerow to another copse then the insect may have already colonised the hedge so the species has a chance of survival.

As hedges often radiate out from woodland edges, they also create a strip-like continuation of the woodland food supply. Squirrels, for example, shunning the exposed fields, make sorties along hedges to forage for hazel nuts. Badgers will come out of a wood to root along hedgebanks for whatever they can find.

Plants which cannot spread across open fields often 'travel' along the base of a well-grown hedgerow. Shade-loving woodland plants such as bluebells and primroses take advantage of the damp and overhanging conditions similar to that of the wood. The seeds of fruit-bearing plants are dispersed along the hedgebank by birds and small mammals, often far away from the parent plant. Most berries are eaten for their fleshy outer coat. The hard seed passes through the animal undamaged, so a solitary blackberry bush can be the source of several other clumps of bushes along a hedge over a period of time.

Larder for animals The special plant community that makes up a mature hedgerow offers a wider range of foodstuffs than most deciduous woodlands, making the hedge a very attractive habitat in winter, particularly for birds. Migratory fieldfares and redwings

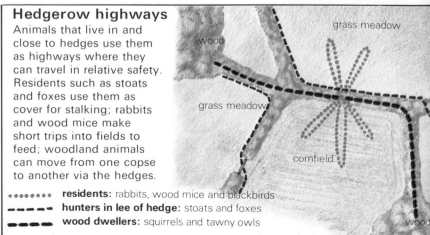

Hedgerow highways
Animals that live in and close to hedges use them as highways where they can travel in relative safety. Residents such as stoats and foxes use them as cover for stalking; rabbits and wood mice make short trips into fields to feed; woodland animals can move from one copse to another via the hedges.

········· **residents:** rabbits, wood mice and blackbirds
– – – – – **hunters in lee of hedge:** stoats and foxes
▬ ▬ ▬ ▬ **wood dwellers:** squirrels and tawny owls

oin blackbirds, thrushes and starlings from home and abroad, and flocks of finches, buntings, sparrows and tits to exploit the seasonal succession of berries and seeds. After glutting on the autumn harvest of elder and blackberries, birds turn to rose-hips and haws, then sloes, and finally to ivy berries. Hips and sloes are taken mostly by thrushes, while agile tits collect the fruits of spindle, honeysuckle and bryony.

In winter, voles, mice and squirrels bury caches of seeds and nuts. Wood mice and bank voles are good climbers and so can get at the berries high up in the hedge. A typical winter menu would include rose-hips, haws, hazel nuts and acorns. With practice, we can learn from seed remains who has been eating them. Wood mice eat only the hard centre of haws, discarding the fleshy coat, while bank voles do just the opposite.

Change of diet This bounty of vegetarian foods allows quite a number of mammals to remain active throughout the winter. But the predators such as weasels and stoats have to be versatile to survive. In winters when the hedgerow fruit crop is poor (hawthorn is very variable), and the rodent populations correspondingly low, predators alter their diet to include roosting birds or even move into nearby woodlands and fields in search of other food.

A few invertebrates also manage to stay

Above: Planted originally to mark boundaries and enclose patches of land, Britain's 350,000 miles of hedgerow provide a vital habitat for wildlife.

How to date a hedgerow
You can estimate the age of a hedge by counting the number of shrub species in a 30m (100ft) stretch. On average it takes 100 years for a new species to become established, so a hedge with four shrub species is likely to be roughly 400 years old.

Above: Like the more common wood mice, the yellow-necked mice are expert climbers, often using old birds' nests high up in hedges as feeding platforms where they have stored nuts and berries.

Right: The brimstone is the only hibernating butterfly you are likely to find in hedge tops. The brightly coloured male is the first to leave the clumps of ivy or holly which have protected it through the winter.

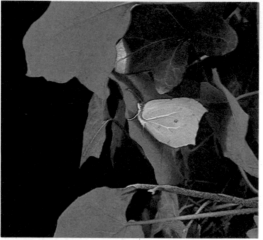

Left: The eating habits of the rabbit have strongly influenced the composition of hedges: hawthorn, elder and nettles, which rabbits find unpalatable, thrive whereas spindle bushes, which they devour, are rare.

Opposite page: Fieldfares come from the Arctic in winter to feed on hedgerow berries and seeds.

Below: St George's mushrooms—they can be found at the base of hedgerows.

active throughout the winter, notably slug which tunnel deep into the hedgebank soil freezing weather sets in. Snails are les adventurous, sealing off the entrance to the shell with a mucus plug and staying put fc the duration of the winter, often in compan with others. Hawthorn is a particularly goo place for finding active invertebrates i winter because it favours growth of lichen and the slimy alga called *Pleurococcus*, bot of which provide food for springtails, barklic and woodlice. A select band of moths— winter moths, spring ushers, pale brindle beauties and mottled umbers—are also activ in winter, laying their eggs at this time. Th most striking feature of the group is that th females are small, wingless, bug-like crea tures, scarcely recognisable as moths at al The ones we see flying around the hedgerov are the amorous males, seeking females o the trunks of trees.

Dormant insects The vast majority o insects overwinter as eggs, larvae, pupae o hibernating adults. A careful examination o any part of the hedge will yield insects: lady birds dormant in thick beds of lichen an crevices in and under bark; earwigs huddle together in the hollow, dead stems of hog weed; the larvae of holly leaf-miner flie inside the blisters on holly leaves.

All of these dormant insects are, of course vulnerable and supplement the vegetarian diet of roving mammals. Shrews take thei toll of buried pupae; wrens, custom-built fo the labyrinthine hedge habitat, mop up spiders' eggs; tits puncture the blisters or holly leaves—just as they peck through milk bottle tops—to extract the larvae of the leaf miner fly.

Wind-breaks As well as providing shelter for over-wintering creatures, the hedge can also act as a wind-break for nearby ploughed fields. In this respect, a permeable hedge is much more efficient at sheltering the land on its leeward (or downwind) side than a solid stone wall. The wind gusts over a solid barrier at the same or even increased speeds, but filters through the shrubs and herbs of a hedge slowly, decreasing in speed and strength as it does so. In turn, this affects humidity, temperature and soil moisture—all very much to the benefit of the ploughed soil (which is not blown away), and to the various crops which are to be planted later on as the differing seasons progress.

Given its sheltered conditions and the fact that it is a great reservoir of wildlife, the hedgerow is one of the best places to look for early signs of spring. From January onwards, the territorial song of the great tit is increasingly heard, soon accompanied by the more lyrical mistle thrush. In February, elder leaves begin to unfold and a sunny day may coax out an early brimstone butterfly. Blackbirds have been known to start nesting in February and some rabbits may be giving birth to their first new generation of the year.

THE WORLD WITHIN A BRAMBLE BUSH

The bramble or wild blackberry is found in scrub, hedgerows and woodland throughout Britain and the thickets it forms are colonized by an enormous range of wild animals who find food, shelter and safety within its thorny, arching branches.

Under the blanket name of 'bramble' lurks confusion almost as tangled as the plant itself. Opinion varies as to whether there is only one bramble, with a multitude of different growth forms, or whether each is truly a distinct type. One authority divides the British brambles into 40 or more species, and over 2000 varieties have been described. But, however many types there are, the bramble or blackberry is immensely successful at colonizing a wide range of soils and habitats throughout the British Isles.

Bramble is, for instance, often the dominant field layer in oak and beech woodland and, though best established in ancient, relict woods, it quickly invades modern plantations and roadsides, its tolerance of shade giving it a major advantage over more sun-loving species. Once bramble has cast its shadow over the woodland floor, few other plants can co-exist with it, except for shade-resistant species such as wood sorrel. Its main associate, however, is bracken, whose fiddleheads can easily snake upwards through the bramble's cat's-cradle of arching shoots.

Right: Brambles can form almost impenetrable thickets, the thorns assisting the branches to clamber over tree branches, shrubs and even fences. Flowers at the tips of stems are the first to set and produce berries. A bramble can bear berries in all stages of ripeness from the hard, pale green ones, through red to the large, luscious shiny black of the ripest fruits. Birds, insects and mammals tend to feed only on the ripe fruits.

Below: This distinctive gall is produced on a bramble stem by the larvae of the gall wasp *Diastrophus rubi*.

Some climbing and trailing plants, notably honeysuckle, also find a solid support in the bramble's trellis-work.

The bramble thicket At first sight a bramble thicket looks as random as an entanglement of barbed wire. But on closer inspection a clear structure reveals itself. A mature thicket has three main layers of 'canes'. On the top there is a thriving leafy zone containing the bulk of the new canopy; these are mostly lateral shoots from the two-year-old canes which, with the remains of the previous year's canopy, form the middle layer. Thirdly there is a leafless bottom layer, containing most of the standing wood and looking grey and lifeless.

Each year's canes grow through the basement layers, eventually falling over under their own weight and that of the canes of subsequent years. Thus the plant scrambles both upwards and outwards over its own ageing understorey. Most canes grow actively for two years before joining the bottom layer. The root stock or root 'crown' of the whole plant is long-lived and continues to send forth new stems for up to about eight years. This new growth is the first line in the bramble's attack on unoccupied ground.

A feast for all Late in the summer, when the

found growing in the old latrine pits near badger setts.

Of the animal species listed, only the tits take the trouble to extract and discard the seeds before eating the pulp. The pulp itself is highly digestible, the seeds passing through the gut of a song thrush in no more than about 40 minutes.

Apart from being carried some distance in this time and, with luck, being deposited in a place suitable for germination, there is a further advantage in the bramble-bird association. Bramble seeds sown in the autumn germinate the following spring, provided they experience freezing in winter. However, it has been shown that seeds which have passed through a thrush's gut germinate considerably quicker than ones sown directly from fresh fruit. It appears that in some way, probably by softening the seed coat, the digestive process hastens germination. This presumably gives eaten seeds a clear advantage in spring when countless seedlings are competing to outgrow their rivals in the race for light and space.

Mammal enemies Not all animals, however, are as obliging as the birds. Mice and voles, with their small incisor teeth, are quite able to crunch up bramble seeds and so may be regarded as enemies. Nevertheless, the prickles are a formidable barrier to many animals. The sharp, recurved thorns tend to prevent small rodents from scaling the stems and such birds as the robin, the thrushes and the long-tailed tit like to build their nests in bramble for this very reason. (However, a weasel has been observed running up the

tems arch over to the ground, their tips can end out roots of their own, producing new daughter plants. However, the bramble's introduction to new habitats is mostly accomplished indirectly by presenting birds and mammals with a bonanza of fruit in the autumn.

The second-year and older canes bear their five-petalled white or pink flowers from May onwards. The flowering season is lengthy and the fruits develop any time from late August to October. The flowers right at the tip of the stem are the first to set and typically produce the plumpest, sweetest fruits. Those further up the stem take perhaps another six weeks to ripen so that, at any one time in late summer, the bramble thicket bears unripe green berries, half-ripe red ones and fully ripe black ones.

The main consumers of bramble berries are among birds marsh and willow tits, bullfinches and, to a lesser extent, blackbirds and song thrushes. Among mammals, foxes, badgers and even squirrels and deer are fond of bramble berries. The berries are sought for their energy-rich pulp, while the seeds within pass undigested through the gut and are conveniently deposited in a 'ready-grow' package of manure. This is why brambles can often be

Left: The wealth of insect life on bramble fruit offers rich pickings for predators such as spiders and insectivorous birds. Garden spiders, like this garden cross spider, ensnare flies and other insects in their elegant orb-webs, while money spiders, such as *Linyphia triangularis*, straddle sheet-like nets across leaves and stems. Eventually, the spiders find themselves, in an oasis of easy prey, slowed down by the chills of advancing autumn, perhaps even intoxicated by the fermenting sap. With the onset of heavy dews and the first frosts, mildew begins to cloud the late berries. In medieval times in England this was a sign that the devil had defiled the crop, and it was therefore deemed unwise to pick blackberries after Michaelmas Day (29 September).

red admiral
butterfly

banded
snail

fruit fly

blotch mine
on leaf caused
by sawfly larva

**bramble
flowers**

tortricid moth
Epiblema

Above and top left: Some
of the wildlife found on
the topmost layer of the
bramble thicket. Red
admiral and ringlet
butterflies, like the
fruit fly, feed on nectar
from the flowers and may
even sip juices from
the over-ripe berries. A
snail may be seen crawling
up the stem, intent on
finding a leaf to feed on.
Blotch mines in the leaves
are the work of the larvae of
such sawflies as *Metallus
rubi*. The pupae of such
moths as *Epiblema* shelter
in silken tents among leaves
drawn together for support.

Left: The five-petalled
white and pink flowers of
the bramble are produced
from May onwards through
a lengthy flowering season.

Below: Serpentine or tunnel
mines produced in bramble
leaves by the larvae of
the pygmy moth *Nepticula
aurella*. The larvae are
safely sandwiched between
the upper and lower layers
of the leaves.

stems of a bramble thicket almost as if the
thorns were the rungs of a ladder; in this
particular case, the bramble's defences were
of no avail to the blackbird's nest sited in the
thicket – the weasel plundered it with ruthless
efficiency.)

Bramble leaves, especially those on the
younger growth not protected by fully developed thorns, suffer considerable damage
from browsing animals, notably in spring
when the new leaves are soft and highly
palatable. But they are probably even more
vulnerable in hard winters. Bramble is not
deciduous and retains its leaves in winter.
These prove remarkably hardy and can with-
stand prolonged exposure to frost and snow.

Being the only bulk herbage available in
winter on the woodland floor, bramble leaves
are taken by a wide variety of animals. After
the severe winter of 1981–82, for example,
the brambles in an Oxfordshire wood showed
signs of heavy browse damage, being virtually
stripped of leaves. Muntjac deer, and possibly
also rabbits and hares, were thought to be
responsible. Studies in the south of England
have shown that fallow and roe deer eat
bramble leaves all year round, but especially
in winter and spring. Among domestic
animals, goats are extremely fond of bramble,
and seem impervious to the prickles as they
mow through the densest thickets.

Insect attack Bramble leaves are also
attacked directly by less obvious agents such

new canopy

previous year's canopy

leafless bottom layer —deep shade

ripe fruit

comma butterfly

bullfinch

...s rust-fungi–and insects. Each insect group ...ay be identified by the sort of damage it ...flicts. Thus leaves that look torn and pep-...ered with holes have been attacked by capsid ...ugs. The peculiar raised blotches or galleries, ...oking rather like worm casts, that appear on ...e undersides of the leaves, are the work of ...arious insect larvae. These larvae, the off-...pring either of sawflies such as *Metallus rubi*, ...r small moths, eat their way through the ...side of the leaf, sandwiched between its ...pper and lower layers. Some larvae munch ...utwards in all directions to form a blister, ...thers along a vein, creating a winding, ...erpentine corridor or tunnel. The mined ...reas of the leaf are often white with frass ...he waste products of the larvae), while ...thers turn a reddish-purple colour.

None of the leaf-mining insects is well ...nown, and their identification is a tricky ...rocess. The pygmy moths (Nepticulidae), ...or example, contain no fewer than 67 leaf-...niners of various British plants, caterpillars ...f *Nepticula aurella* commonly tunnelling the ...hitish corridors often seen in bramble leaves.

Nepticula larvae spin a saucer-shaped ...ocoon in which to pupate. These are readily ...istinguishable from those built by pupal ...ortricid moths like *Epiblema*, whose cater-...illars, emerging from hibernation in spring, ...nove to the tip of a bramble shoot and draw ...he leaves together as supports for a volum-...nous silken tent, painstakingly spun as a

Above: A cluster of ripe (black) and semi-ripe (red) blackberries on a thorny stem. The many individual segments of the berry are attached to a hard white central core. Each segment contains a single seed.

Above right: A bramble thicket has three layers of canes – a leafy top zone, the previous year's canopy and a leafless bottom layer.

Right and below: Bramble thicket inhabitants nearer the ground: flesh flies such as the greenbottle feed on the juices of decaying berries as, too, do wasps and the comma butterfly. Capsid bugs attack the leaves, as do the leaf-mining larvae of some small moths. The bullfinch is among many birds that feed on the autumn bounty of berries, while the garden cross spider sits in the centre of her orb-web, waiting for passing insects to be trapped. The white grubs of the raspberry beetle can often be found feeding inside the berries.

common wasp

capsid bug

raspberry beetle larva

decaying fruit

greenbottle fly

serpentine leaf mine caused by pygmy moth larva

rust-fungus

garden cross spider and web

pupal chamber.

Even the tough-looking bramble canes are not immune from house-hunting insects. The small gall wasp *Diastrophus rubi* is responsible for the somewhat S-shaped swellings 5-20cm (2-8in) long sometimes found on the stems of bramble. These may be found in any month of the year, varying in colour from green in the early stages, through reddish, to brown at maturity.

The female gall wasp pierces the skin of the stem to lay a batch of 80 eggs or more. When they hatch, the movements of the larvae have an irritant effect on the bramble tissue, which reacts by swelling into a gall. Each larva gouges out a tiny chamber for itself as it eats the gall tissues, so that in vertical section the gall comes to resemble a block of flats. By November, if all goes well, the development of this crowded nursery is complete, and the larvae pupate inside, to emerge as adult wasps in spring.

The larvae within their gall look perfectly secure, but are in fact vulnerable to being parasitised by other species of wasp closely related to themselves. These parasites lay their eggs not in the bramble tissue but in the bodies of the gall wasp larvae, which then become gruesome larders for the parasite

Above: One of many insect visitors to bramble flowers—a silver-washed fritillary.

Opposite page: Red admiral butterfly on blackberries.

Below: Dormice and nest in a bramble thicket.

species' own offspring.

Autumn invaders In September inviting clusters of shiny black berries are hanging from the older shoots. These provide sugary sap for a constant stream of insect traffic. Wasps, their nesting and working duties over for the year, are often the first to pierce the skin of the berries, allowing a host of green bottles and other flesh flies to glut themselves on the oozing juices. It seems that carrion flies sip blackberry juices as they search for corpses in which to lay their eggs, and it may also help some to build up their energy stores for overwintering.

Much more attractive visitors are the butterflies—notably the comma, speckled wood and ringlet, and the autumn specialist, the red admiral. Few insects, fortunately, live right inside the berries, although the raspberry beetle *Byturus tomentosus* does so, the larvae emerging from eggs laid in the flowers to feast on the developing fruit. Anyone picking and eating blackberries from the hedgerow may well have noticed these larvae—they look like tiny white worms.

An old favourite Despite its prickly thorns, the bramble, a member of the rose family, is as much loved a wild plant as its more decorative relative, the wild rose. Its widespread value to country people as a medicinal herb, a source of refreshing tea and above all as a generous bearer of fruit, dates back to prehistoric times—as testified by blackberry seeds found in the stomach of Neolithic man disinterred from Essex clay. The fruit is a favourite made into jam or jelly, or used in a variety of pies and tarts.

In bygone days, bramble—in common with many other thorny shrubs and trees—was also believed to be an auspicious plant, a powerful talisman against evil forces. The familiarity of bramble to country people, and their healthy regard for it, is celebrated to this day in a host of colourful local names—cock-brumble, brummelty kites and lady garten berries, to name just a few.

RICH BUT THREATENED WORLD OF DOWNLAND

Chalk grasslands, boasting some 60 exclusive flowering plants as well as a fascinating range of insects, have become one of our most threatened habitats. In Wiltshire alone more than 64,000 acres were ploughed up between 1937 and 1971. Such disturbance ruins the diversity of downland plant life.

Chalk hills with their short, springy, thyme-scented turf, skylarks overhead and sweeping views over the smooth-contoured slopes to the clay vales below are the epitome of what most people think of as downland.

Limestone rocks outcrop over much of the British Isles and the Chalk is the most extensive and recently formed of the four major limestone formations. It is a soft white limestone laid down in the Cretaceous period some 135 to 65 million years ago and now exposed in a great arc from the Yorkshire Wolds to the Dorset Downs. In much of the Wolds and East Anglia it is overlaid by glacial and other more recent deposits and most of the flatter land is under arable cultivation. In the Chilterns there are steeper escarpments with thinner superficial deposits bearing more typical downland scenery. The outcrop passes through the Berkshire Downs to the great chalk massif of Salisbury Plain and the other Wiltshire uplands. The Chalk extends eastwards along the North and South Downs, which culminate at the Channel coast as the white cliffs of Dover and Beachy Head.

Limestones are sedimentary rocks (originally part of the seabed) formed largely from the shells and skeletons of marine invertebrates. Fossils of shell fish, sea urchins, corals and microscopic planktonic animals and plants are common in them. The species represented are those of clear shallow seas and, in the absence of sandy or muddy inflows, the sediments formed consist almost entirely of calcium carbonate. The landforms, soils, vegetation, and even to some extent the animals of downland and other limestone country, all owe their characteristic nature to this unique purity of chemical rock composition (chalk usually consists of from 95% to 99% calcium carbonate) and to its properties.

No surface water Calcium carbonate is only slightly soluble in pure water, but much more so in weak acids. Rainwater that has absorbed carbon dioxide from the atmosphere is an acid solution, so chalk is easily dissolved by rain. Water also passes directly into the permeable rock, or through it in channels, faults and joints, leaving none at the surface. Downland is therefore mostly devoid of ponds and lakes or streams, with much of its drainage underground.

In the past the lack of water made it difficult for shepherds to graze sheep, so they made dew ponds; these were recharged by condensation from the atmosphere. To keep the pond and its water cool, the shepherds insulated it from the heat-retaining ground with a thick layer of straw. They mixed clay with water and then trampled on it, spreading this wet clay over the straw to keep the water in.

True downland soils are very thin and made up almost exclusively of black or greyish organic plant and animal remains. When the land is ploughed they can disappear almost entirely, leaving sparkling white fields where the chalk bedrock just below is exposed.

Abundance of flowers The short thick grass (sward) of chalk downs contains one of the richest associations of flowering plants found in the British Isles. In a close-grazed patch a metre or so square you might find as many

bove: The village of
oynings nestles in a valley
etween the chalk hills of
ne South Downs in Sussex.
he hill in the foreground,
lose-grazed by sheep, is
overed with ant hills. The
ellow field ants build these
omes on chalk grasslands,
nd the domes sometimes
urvive for centuries. Wild
nyme often thrives on these
ry hillocks.

here are few wildlife
pectacles more impressive
nan drifts of silvery blue
utterflies flitting in the
ummer sun over chalk hills.
he chalkhill blue is on the
ving in July and August.
his one is resting on a
reater knapweed flower.

as 30 or 40 species. Most of these species
are plants other than grasses and in some
places the sward is so dominated by these
rosette, trailing and cushion plants that the
word grassland is almost a misnomer.

The great diversity of species in chalk
grasslands is made possible by the absence of
limiting factors such as toxic elements to
which only a few species have become adapted
(as is the case, for example, in acid heath-
lands). Also, the infertility of the soil prevents
vigorous species getting the upper hand.

But how do these lime-loving plants
(calcicoles) of the downlands avoid competing
with one another? In fact, what seems superficially to be a rather uniform environment
is not; nor do all the species exploit it in the
same way. Over 90% of chalk grassland plants
are perennials, but of very different kinds.
Some, like the orchids and dropwort, overwinter underground as tubers; others, such
as rock-roses and thymes, are dwarf evergreen woody shrubs. Some, like squinancy-
wort and lady's bedstraw, are trailing plants

and others, like dwarf thistle and plantains,
are rosette plants.

These different perennial growth forms
make different demands on the environment,
as do the few annuals such as fairy flax and
yellow-wort and biennials such as autumn
gentian. The various kinds of plants have
different flowering times, amounts of seeds,
times of germination and germination needs.
Bare soil, for example, is particularly important to the annuals and biennials. Many of
the perennials are surprisingly long-lived,
maybe up to 100 years. But their differing
flowering times, from the spring orchids to
the autumn gentians, and individual kinds
of seed production suggest that they probably
have quite different cycles of regeneration,
even if their demands on the environment
as mature plants may be somewhat similar.

Invertebrate life The great diversity of
downland plants is reflected in a considerable
range of invertebrates, for many of them,
particularly the insects, have specific food
plant needs. Many of the butterflies and

moths of downland are rare elsewhere for this reason. The chalkhill blue butterfly is perhaps, more than any other species, the symbol of the southern downlands. The food plant of its caterpillars (and of the rarer adonis blue) is the horseshoe vetch, a strict calcicole, so the butterfly, like its food plant, is confined to downlands. The larvae of the brown argus butterfly–also grouped with the 'blues'–feed almost exclusively on the rock-rose.

Most remarkable of all this group of closely related blue butterflies is the large blue. Its caterpillar first feeds on wild thyme, but is then taken by ants into their nests, where they milk it for a secretion it produces; the caterpillar in turn feeds on ant larvae. Wild thyme is not restricted to downland, but the limestone hills of the Cotswolds were one of the strongholds of the large blue before it began to become extremely rare, if not extinct. Its disappearance was caused by changes in, and loss of, habitat.

Some of the other characteristic butterflies and moths of downland also occur more widely wherever their food plants grow. The large and silver-spotted skippers and the marbled white feed on fescue and other grasses, while the six-spot burnet moth favours vetches and clovers, especially bird's-foot-trefoil.

The need for calcium Some invertebrates are even more directly tied to chalky soils than these butterflies and moths. Earthworms require calcium and are thus much more common in alkaline than acid soils, though they are only frequent in the deeper down-land soils. Snails need calcium for their shells and are likewise common on chalky soils, particularly the banded snails.

The larger animals of downland are less diverse than the invertebrates and less con-fined to it. Small mammals, such as short-tailed field voles and the common and pygmy shrews, which are widely distributed in all kinds of grassland, are also common on downland, particularly in the taller grasses and open scrub. They form a main food source for stoats and weasels, and also kestrels, perhaps the typical downland bird.

Above: Glow-worms form part of the chalk downland foodchain. Their larvae feed on snails, which thrive on chalky soils, by injecting them with digestive juices, then sucking up the remains. The adults, shown here, hardly feed at all.

At one time, when there were vast unbroke tracts of grassland on the southern down lands, other large birds such as the Montagu harrier, stone curlew and great bustard wer also found there. But the harrier and ston curlew are now very rare and the bustar became extinct in Britain as a breeding bird.

Skylarks, meadowpipits and wheatears a nest on downland and feed on the abundar supply of seeds and invertebrates. Wheatea are now more common in the north, but the were once so common on the South Down that shepherds found it a profitable sidelin to trap them in the abandoned rabbit burrow that wheatears use for nesting. They sold the as a delicacy for the table on the south coas Today, of course, these small birds no long feature as an item on the menu.

The absence of water from downlan means that amphibians like frogs, toads an newts are rare, as are grass snakes whic prey on them. But most of our reptiles, suc as slow worms and common lizards, whic need warmth to become active, thrive on th dry, warm downland slopes.

Above: This colourful patch of chalk grassland in Hampshire contains a mixture of grasses, pyramida orchids, ox-eye daisies, lady's bedstraw and the dandelion look-alike, hawkbit.

Right: Thistles abound among the short turf of chal downland.

Left: The velvety flowers of the bee orchid look strikingl like bumble bees.

HOW THE DOWNS KEEP THEIR SHAPE

Grazing animals–mainly sheep and rabbits–play a vital role in keeping the rich mixture of flowering plants on chalk grasslands. Without them scrub would invade, smothering the plants and forcing out the creatures dependent on them.

Above: Sheep graze the chalk grassland on Aston Rowant National Nature Reserve in the Chilterns.

Downlands owe much of their character to the presence of large grazing animals. Rabbits and domestic stock, principally sheep, are the main agents by which downland is kept open. Hares, though common, rarely occur in sufficient numbers to have a marked effect on the vegetation. Nor do fallow or roe deer. Even though they often browse

scrub around wood edges, they rarely venture far on to the open downland. It is possible that great herds of large wild herbivores, such as wild cattle, were responsible, in conjunction with lightning fires, for keeping downland open in the early post-glacial period some 12,000 years ago, just as buffalo or bison maintained the North American prairies. But for most of their history our downlands have been maintained by grazing sheep.

Close grazing by sheep or rabbits prevents the grassland from being colonised by shrubs and trees. It does this in two ways. Shrubs and trees, with their growing points in exposed buds, are more vulnerable to grazing than small grasses and flowering plants which have growing points protected in buds on or in the ground. These plants can rapidly replace parts eaten by animals, but woody plants cannot. Secondly, grazing animals remove nutrients from the environment which the bigger and more nutrient-demanding shrub species need. The traditional pattern of downland grazing was to drift the

grazed in the spring, just as moorlands are still burnt in the North. Provided only small areas are burnt at a time little damage is done to the plants and animals. Most are steppe or prairie species which can sustain the quite natural lightning fires that flare up across arid grasslands from time to time.

Areas of existing downland are still maintained to some extent by burning, particularly in the Cotswolds and Dorset Downs. Other parts–especially in Wiltshire, Hampshire and parts of Sussex–are still managed in the traditional way by grazing, despite the enormous pressure for the land to be ploughed up or fertilized. Some of these areas are owned by farmers who have always kept stock and do not want to change over to arable land, even though it would be more profitable. Others are owned by conservation bodies, such as the Nature Conservancy Council and the National Trust, who intentionally maintain the diversity of the vegetation by giving local farmers licences to graze it. Further stretches of downland are maintained almost by accident: they are areas such as Salisbury Plain, owned by the Ministry of Defence, where tenant farmers are allowed to graze their sheep because the bomb-filled land cannot be ploughed.

Need for food However, this existing species-rich downland is under continual threat. The extent of downland has fluctuated over the years with changes in the rural

Chalk outcrops

Chalk grassland is the typical habitat covering these outcrops, with the exception of the sandy heath of the Breckland.
1 Wolds 2 Breckland
3 East Anglian chalk
4 Chilterns 5 Berkshire Downs 6 Salisbury Plain
7 Hampshire Downs
8 North Downs 9 South Downs.

Below: Though common as a garden plant the pasque flower is quite rare in the wild. It can still be found on the chalk hills of the Chilterns and East Anglia, and on other limestone grasslands.

ocks of sheep over the hills in the day and hen bring them down into the cultivated elds in the valleys at night.

This sytem of unenclosed grazing (pastoralism) was different from most agriculture ecause nutrients removed in the form of mutton, wool or dung left in the valleys, were ot replaced on the hills by fertilisers. The utrients had to build up again naturally rom rain and the minerals from the underlying rock. Since this was a very slow process, ownlands were infertile and good only for ght grazing followed by a period of no razing. Their value lay in their great extent, o that although inherently unproductive in ny particular part, in total they were very roductive.

Burning the grassland Fire has a similar ffect on downland vegetation to grazing. Woody species are more vulnerable to being urned and recover less readily than do rasses and small non-woody plants. In the ast it was common practice to burn coarse rass and scrub on downland at the end of the vinter to provide fresh new growth to be

Above: The wart-biter, which can give a painful nip with its strong mandibles, is one of our biggest and rarest bush crickets. It lives in long grass at the edge of chalk downland.

Right: The wheatear needs extensive tracts of open land to survive and so is only found on the larger areas of downland.

Below: The exposed chalk bedrock gives the White Horse on the Pewsey Downs, Wiltshire, its bright outline. Flora such as orchids, rock-roses and harebells flourish on these downs.

economy. During the Napoleonic Wars t blockade and higher food prices made worthwhile for farmers to bring more la under cultivation. Development in agric tural technology, such as better knowledge rotation and manuring, enabled infert downlands to become much more producti

Parliamentary enclosure acts brought mu land previously managed as common la under the direct control of single landowne Large areas of downland were burnt befc being ploughed up. As a result, many dow land species became rare or extinct. T pasque flower and monkey orchid, for e ample, disappeared from many of th known localities. The monkey orchid w thought to have become extinct until a sing and then a second, colony were rediscover in the 1950s.

With the repeal of the Corn Laws in 18 and the subsequent flow of grain from Nor America and the colonies, agriculture we into decline. Much downland went back pasture, the abandoned fields being large grazed by enormous populations of rabbits

The blockade of the Second World W had the same effect as that of earlier war large areas of downland were ploughed increased home production of food. T Agricultural Act of 1947, with its subsidi for food production, maintained agricultur prosperity and ever since the war there h been a continual loss of downland to arab farming or pastures that are reseeded ar then enclosed.

Invasion by scrub A further blow for tl future of downlands was the arrival myxomatosis in the mid-1950s which almo eliminated the vast rabbit populations. Coar grass and scrub invaded from the richer vall and plateau soils. You can still see many the old warren sites on the downs from tl bright green nitrogen-rich vegetation c them. These are often clumps of nutrien demanding species such as elder, nettles ar brambles.

A small patch of chalk grassland manage in the traditional, impoverishing way m contain as many as 60 to 80 species of plan and up to 25 species of butterfly. Grasslan 'improved' by fertilisers contains only 2 or species, which have smothered the othe plants, and no species of butterfly.

If we want to hold on to our stretches c open downland, with their special plant an animal communities, we will have to mak sure that the remaining downs are managec Some people find it difficult to see why suc an 'unnatural' habitat should be conserve at all. Unnatural it may be in that domesti stock are needed to maintain the diversity c plants and to keep the invading scrub ou But the sheep have only taken over the role c wild grazing animals which Man has elimin ated and which still maintain similar grass lands, such as steppes and prairies, in othe parts of the world.

ANCIENT & MODERN HAYMEADOWS

raditional haymaking, which allows many flowers to
set their seeds before cutting begins, ensures a
glorious mixture of grasses and flowers every year,
and consequently a rich insect life. But modern
meadows only contain a few grasses and little wildlife.

is Perthshire haymeadow
being baled in early July.
e hay is first cut and left to
y on the ground.
epending on the weather,
is may take a few days or a
uple of weeks. The
eadow can then be left for
second crop of hay or for
azing, or might even be
oughed up and sown with
arable crop.

A true meadow is a field in which the grasses
and other plants are allowed to grow up in
the summer and are then cut for hay. Often,
however, the word meadow is used for any
kind of grassy field, and in order to distinguish
the true meadows it is better to refer to them
as haymeadows or simply hayfields.

Haymaking is the traditional way of
obtaining winter feed for cattle and other
livestock, and it has been carried out for
centuries. The grasses and associated plants
are cut while they are still green, and trad-

itionally they are dried in the sun, although
the final stages of drying may be completed in
a barn. Cutting normally takes place just as
the grasses are coming into flower, which
means during June and July in most parts of
the country. If cutting is delayed until after
flowering, the hay has a lower protein content and is less digestible. Earlier harvesting,
on the other hand, means lower yields because the plants are smaller.

The taking of a hay crop in June or July
allows many spring flowers to flourish in the
meadows and to set their seeds before cutting
begins. Some autumn-flowering species, such
as the meadow saffron, a crocus-like flower
which appears in September, are also un-
affected by the haymaking. The traditional
haymeadows, which were often used for
nothing else, were thus a riot of colour in both
spring and autumn; several summer-flowering perennials even managed to survive there
as well. Even moderate grazing in early spring
and again after haymaking did not reduce
the rich plant life of the meadows.

Ancient meadows In view of the increased
hay yields resulting from agricultural im-
provements such as draining, re-seeding and
fertilising, it is perhaps surprising that there
are any 'unimproved' meadows left at all. But

there are a few ancient meadows which have probably never been ploughed, drained, or fertilised. They have always been used as hayfields and they carry the very wide range of plants associated with the traditional management. Most of them are to be found in the upper parts of the Thames Valley and in Suffolk, usually on the moister soils of the valley bottoms. Some of the old Thames Valley meadows are Lammas Lands, on which the villagers have grazing rights after haymaking (Lammas was a harvest festival that took place on the first of August). The farmers also take the hay on an allotment system, and the complex legal situation concerning ownership has deterred anyone from

Left: A common butterfly of haymeadows, particularly their edges, is the gatekeeper or hedge brown. This species is easily told apart from its close relative, the meadow brown, by its broad orange markings and smaller size. The eye spots near the wing margins act as decoys for predatory birds, deflecting their attacks away from the vulnerable body of the butterfly. It is quite common to find a gatekeeper butterfly with a peck marked wing.

Left: Leys, that is, fields which are ploughed and sown with a few grasses, have a bluish tinge quite different from the yellowish green of traditional meadows. This is largely due to the amount of fertiliser sprayed on them. This one has perennial rye grass.

Below: Traditional meadows, such as this one in Teesdale, allow grasses and wild flowers to grow together. Here you can see red clover, yellow rattle, ox-eye daisies and buttercups.

trying to improve the meadows – with obvious benefits to the wild flowers and to conservation in general. Elsewhere, most of the meadows have survived simply because farmers have been content to follow the traditional methods of hayfield management. Most of these meadows are now cherished nature reserves.

The most famous flower associated with old lowland meadows is the fritillary, also known as the snake's head fritillary because of the resemblance of the unopened flower to a snake's head. Once known in at least 27 of Britain's counties, this bulbous plant now grows wild in no more than about 20 meadows, but where it does survive it can often be seen in immense numbers.

Other spring-flowering species found regularly in ancient haymeadows include cuckoo flower, cowslip, dandelion, wild daffodil, early-purple orchid and green-winged orchid. These all scatter their seeds before the hay crop is taken. Later-flowering species which occur regularly include yellow rattle, oxeye daisy, red and white clovers, and pepper saxifrage. The latter is a yellow-flowered umbellifer and it is one of the first species to disappear when the grassland is 'improved'.

These summer-flowering plants survive under traditional haymeadow management because they can throw up a second crop of flowers after the cut in meadows which are not grazed. The cut is usually fairly high – about 3-4in (8-10cm) from the ground – and it stimulates fresh growth from the base. Some of the plants can also set a certain amount of seed before the hay is cut. Later flowering species are not common on Lammas land because of the grazing but ungrazed hayfields may carry the beautiful meadow saffron.

Swarming with life Animal life is abundant in ancient meadows, but none of the animals is confined to these old grasslands. Among the larger animals, rabbits are the most common so long as there is sufficient cover for them along the edges of the fields. Hares also frequent the meadows, and large numbers of voles inhabit the turf. Skylarks nest on the ground, and many other birds, including strels, come to the meadows to feed.

It is, however, the smaller animals – the insects and other invertebrates – that are most numerous in the haymeadows. Familiar butterflies include the meadow brown and wall heath, both of which feed on grasses in the larval (caterpillar) stage, and the common blue, whose caterpillars feed on bird's-foot-trefoil and other legumes. The small copper is another common inhabitant, its caterpillars feeding on sorrel. Grasshoppers of several species advertise their presence with buzzing courtship songs during the summer, and the grasses also teem with small beetles and hoppers. Bumble bees buzz from flower to flower as they gather nectar and pollen, and many nest in the ground or among the bases of the grasses. Spiders are abundant everywhere, feeding on the wide variety of insect life. They are there throughout the year, but their sheet webs show up best on autumn mornings when covered with dew.

Limestone meadows The dales of Yorkshire and other parts of the Pennines support some very special kinds of haymeadows with an extremely rich variety of flowers. These meadows occur on limestone at altitudes between about 210 and 300m (700 and 1000ft) and, like the lowland meadows, they have been cut for hay for hundreds of years. They are heavily grazed in spring, and their flowers are at their best in June and July. Because of the spring grazing, the vegetation has not grown enough to be cut for hay until well into July, and by then many of the flowers have set seed and ensured their survival in the meadows. Among these flowers are many of the common species found in the lowland meadows together with some more northern specialities such as wood crane's-bill, globeflower, and melancholy thistle. Several southern flowers, such as the fritillary and the green-winged orchid, are absent from the northern meadows.

The mammal and bird life in the dales meadows is very similar to that of the lowland meadows, but there are differences in the insect life. In general, because of the colder climate, there are fewer species in the northern meadows, but there are some such as the metallic-coloured click beetles (*Corymbites*) which are particularly characteristic of the dales.

Improved meadows Most meadows have been improved by drainage and by the regular application of fertilisers. These give increased hay yields at the expense of the wild flowers. They all belong to the immense category known as permanent grassland which includes the grazing pastures. Many fields are both cut for hay and grazed. Sometimes there is more than one hay cut in a year.

Although more plentiful than the hay from unimproved meadows the hay from improved meadows still contains many plants such as bent grasses which are of poor nutritional value to the livestock. Other plants include

Above: This meadow, full of meadow buttercups, has probably been previously grazed by cattle. The buttercups, which are poisonous to cattle, are left. Once the hay is cut and dried the buttercups lose their poison and can be eaten with the grasses.

Left: The meadow grasshopper is the only British grasshopper that cannot fly.

white clover, plantains, bulbous and meadow buttercups, daisies, dandelions and yarrow. The exact composition of these grasslands depends on the soil and also on the relative amounts of grazing and cutting. The insect life in them is similar to that in the more flowery meadows, but there are fewer species.

The most productive fields are the temporary meadows known as leys – meadows which are ploughed up and re-seeded every few years – and much of today's hay is grown in them. They are sown with just a few (or only one) of the most nutritious and fast-growing grasses, with or without clover. Perennial rye, Italian rye, cock's-foot, timothy and meadow fescue are the main grasses used for leys. Compared with the meadows already described, they support little animal life; even grasshoppers shun the tall, dense stands of grass because they need to lay their eggs in bare patches of soil.

Although leys are highly productive at first, 'weed' species gradually invade them and reduce the hay quality after three or four years. The leys are then usually ploughed up and re-seeded or planted with other crops such as cereals. If they are left for eight years or so, many of the better grasses are replaced by bents and other less nutritious species.

Main grasses in ancient haymeadows
Many kinds of grass can be found in old meadows, but the following are some of the most characteristic: soft brome, meadow brome, perennial rye, cock's-foot, Yorkshire fog, yellow oat, false oat, meadow foxtail, sweet vernal grass.
Sweet vernal grass is a very early flowerer and its foliage is strongly scented with a substance called coumarin. It is coumarin that gives new-mown hay its sweet smell.

THE DISTURBED WORLD UNDER THE PLOUGH

Ploughing, sowing and harvesting mean constant interruption for animals and plants. Some creatures, such as cockchafer grubs, survive in the ground from year to year, but the majority are temporary residents, using the fields as a source of food and, once the crops have sprung up, shelter.

Arable land is used for growing crops and, by definition, is regularly ploughed, although ploughing may not take place every year. As such it is a highly artificial, man-made habitat dominated of course by the planted crops from which some animals and birds profit. However modern farming methods, pesticides and weedkillers are changing the balance.

Approximately one third of the surface of the British Isles is covered by arable land, the bulk of it lying on the eastern side of the country. The climate here is drier than in the west–less than 60cm (25in) of rain per year in many parts of East Anglia, compared with more than 100cm (40in) per year for most of Wales–and the land is more easily ploughed. The relatively sunny summers of the eastern regions are also ideal for the ripening of cereals, which are the most widespread and important of the arable crops. The wetter climate and milder winters of western Britain and most of Ireland is conducive to round-the-year grass growth and the land carries a high proportion of permanent grass in the form of grazing pastures, which rarely or never see the plough.

Crop rotation Arable farming was traditionally based on the rotation of crops, with no field carrying the same crop in successive years. The main advantages of such a system are that pests do not get a chance to build up from year to year and the soil minerals are less quickly exhausted because different crops take different proportions of minerals. Some crops, primarily the clovers and other legumes such as peas and beans, actually put nitrates back into the soil through the action of bacteria in their roots. Despite the advantages of crop rotation, however, there is today a tendency to specialise in just a few crops. Some farmers now grow nothing but cereals, with perhaps just an occasional legume crop to help soil fertility. This method of farming is known as 'monoculture'. Administration and machinery costs are reduced, but there is extra expenditure in chemicals to keep the pests under control and to maintain the fertility of the soil. The majority of farmers spray their fields carefully. Spraying at the wrong time (for example in windy weather) or in the wrong place could kill off large numbers of bees, butterflies and beetles.

Preparing the soil Whenever possible, the farmers like to get their ploughing done in the autumn, as soon as the previous crop is harvested. Recently there has been a marked trend towards winter sowing of crops such as wheat or barley rather than spring sowing. The yields are usually higher and there is greater resistance to pests such as thrips, aphids and wireworms, diseases and drought because by spring and early summer the shoots are already well-established. Where crops such as sugar beet are lifted late, or when the autumn is very wet, it is not possible to get the soil into condition for autumn sowing, but ploughing is still worthwhile if the ground is not too wet. The winter frosts can then get to work to break up the clods, and spring harrowing soon produces a fine tilth for seed-sowing.

Rolling in the seed is a common spring-time operation, especially on the lighter soils; autumn-sown cereals are also usually rolled in the spring. The roller breaks the

Above: In early summer the cereal crops are still green. Tractor lines are visible in the foreground where the machines have been used for spraying fertilizers or weedkillers.

Left: Sugar beet harvesting. Root crops such as this account for about 15% of our arable land. The harvesters cut off the tops (which are used as animal fodder) and then lift the white tapered roots, from which sugar is extracted. In the growing of such crops the farmer has, of course, to wage perpetual war against nibbling mammals, an army of insects, and also weeds which would rob the crop of valuable nutrients.

young shoots, but new side shoots quickly appear and a plant which may have had one or two shoots initially may end up with five or six, each of which will produce an ear of grain. Most crops are also sprayed with fertilisers and selective weedkillers in spring—sometimes from the air, but more often with tractor-operated spraying machines. Even potatoes and sugar beet, which used to be hoed by hand and by tractor, are sprayed with chemicals.

Artificial habitat Arable land is clearly a very artificial and highly disturbed community—or, more accurately, a collection of communities. Weeds are the most visible colonizers, many of them actually appearing in the fields before the crops show through the soil; if no control measures are taken, they can completely swamp the crops. More than 200 species of wild plants have been recorded on arable land, most of them annuals. Their seeds germinate in spring and the new plants flower and set their own seeds before harvest.

Some species actually produce two or more generations during the summer. The seeds survive the plough and produce a new crop of weeds in the following spring. These annual weeds are rarely found in permanent pastures because they need bare ground in which to establish themselves.

War on weeds Common annuals found on arable land include poppies, scarlet pimpernel, fumitory, fat hen, charlock and scentless mayweed. Herbicides can be used to kill off all these weeds and today's fields are far less weedy than those of earlier times; but new weed crops still spring up every year. Some of the seeds blow in from elsewhere; others arrive as impurities in the crop seed, although this is a far less common occurrence than it used to be because the seed is carefully screened. Corncockle and cornflower, for example, used to be common cornfield flowers; their seeds, larger than those of many other weeds, were returned to the soil with the cereal seeds the next year. Because of

their efficient screening they are now rare[ly] seen.

Most of the annual weeds come from see[ds] which have been buried in the soil and whi[ch] are brought to the surface by the plough. T[he] brilliant red poppies are among the be[st] examples. Their seeds can remain dormant f[or] many years, and drifts of poppies oft[en] appear after deep ploughing.

Perennial plants cannot normally exist [in] arable land because they are killed by t[he] annual cultivations. There are, howeve[r,] some exceptions, most of which have creepi[ng] roots or underground stems. The ploug[h] chops them into pieces, but each piece ca[n] grow into a new plant. Creeping thistle an[d] field bindweed are among the commonest [of] these weeds, the bindweed often climbing u[p] cereal stems at the edge of the field.

Invaders Like perennial weeds, worms an[d] various soil-dwelling insect grubs, such a[s] leatherjackets and cockchafer larvae, surviv[e] in the ground from year to year. Howeve[r,] most animal life moves into the arable field[s] each year – usually in the spring. The aphid[s] are among the first to go in, having spent th[e] winter as eggs on trees and shrubs in th[e] surrounding hedges and woods. The blac[k] bean aphid overwinters mainly on spindl[e] trees; when the eggs hatch early in spring th[e] aphids feed by sucking sap from the bud[s.] They reproduce quickly and soon sprea[d] into bean and sugar beet fields. Here the[y] reproduce even more quickly and larg[e] colonies soon build up. They are all female[s] and give birth to youngsters without matin[g.] One reason for the rapid population explosio[n] is that all individuals can give birth: anothe[r] is that, with food surrounding them on ever[y] side, the insects can concentrate all thei[r] energies on reproduction.

Rose-grain aphids also invade the grai[n]

Above: Long lines of poppies have sprung up across fields in recent years after the laying of new gas pipes. This is because their seeds, buried deep in the soil, have been brought to the surface by the mechanical diggers.

Right: This skylark is not feeding the young, despite their gaping mouths: it is removing a faecal sac containing their droppings. It will deposit the white sac away from the nest so as not to draw predators' attention to the young.

ds. The fact that they spread from the hedgerows is sometimes used to support the argument for removing hedges, but the hedgerows, of course, also harbour the aphids' enemies in the form of ladybirds and lacewings. These insects soon spread into the fields themselves and normally keep the aphids under control. Just how well the ladybirds do this was shown in the winter of 1978-9 when the extreme cold killed off most of the hibernating ladybirds. The result was an enormous plague of rose-grain aphids towards the end of July.

Birds of the fields Lapwings, rooks and many other birds visit the fields in spring to feed on cockchafer grubs and other soil-dwelling animals; but few of them actually feed on the growing crops, moving away to other feeding grounds when the plants spring up and hide the soil. One notable exception is the woodpigeon, which feeds largely on the leaves of clovers and brassicas (such as kale, cauliflower and cabbage) in winter and spring and on cereals in spring and early summer. The crops often suffer noticeable damage, however, because the birds feed in large flocks. Pheasants and partridges also eat leaves in spring and can often be seen strutting out of the roadside fields. Both species eat the leaves of peas and cereals, although damage is not great, and the partridge also eats plenty of weed leaves. Whereas pheasants prefer to nest in the shelter of shrubs, the partridge is quite happy to nest among the cereals and other crops.

A characteristic bird of the arable fields is the skylark. This familiar songster can be seen and heard high above the fields at any time of the year, although the song is at its best from February to July. During this period the males establish and defend their territories by rising high above them and pouring out their shrill, warbling songs for several minutes at a stretch.

Nibbling mammals The best known of the mammals associated with arable land in spring is the March hare. Bare patches in the middle of cereal fields are often the result of constant grazing of young plants by hares. Rabbits do similar damage, but normally on the edges of the fields, for rabbits do not like to roam too far from the shelter of woods or hedgerows.

Voles and wood mice make frequent sorties into the fields from the surrounding hedgerows and feed on both crops and small creatures; but they do not really live on the arable land. The real denizen of the cornfields is the delightful harvest mouse, which performs some truly amazing antics on the stalks with the aid of its prehensile tail. Its ball-shaped nest, supported by several stalks, was a common sight when the cereals were harvested by hand; but the combines give the animals less time to escape and the harvest mouse is now much less frequent in fields.

The Cockchafer

Also known as the may-bug because the adults are abundant during May, the cockchafer *(Melolontha melolontha)* is a sturdy beetle about 2.5cm (1in) long. It has hard, brick-red wing cases and large, fan-like antennae. The fat white grubs, permanently curved into a 'C' shape and equipped with strong jaws, inflict severe damage on cereals and other arable crops, and are also pests in hay meadows. The female cockchafer tunnels into the soil to a depth of about 20cm (8in) to lay her eggs, and the grubs soon begin their three or four-year feast of roots. They do relatively little damage during the first year because they are small, but the older grubs have amazing appetites and each can destroy scores of plants. Ploughing in early autumn can reduce the population of cockchafer grubs in the soil; then the grubs are fairly near the

Adult cockchafer beetle

Cockchafer grub

surface and large numbers are turned up for the birds to eat. Lapwings, gulls and rooks all enjoy a meal of cockchafer grubs (which are called rook-worms in some places) and have no trouble in digging them out of the soil with their stout beaks. Winter ploughing has less effect on the population because the grubs usually tunnel down below the depth of the plough to avoid the cold. Hay meadows suffer more cockchafer damage than cereals because they are not ploughed each year.

The cockchafer grubs pupate at the end of their third or fourth summer, usually about 60cm (2ft) below the soil surface. The adults emerge from the pupae during the winter, but remain underground until late April or May, when they come out to feed on the leaves of many kinds of deciduous trees, often causing severe damage in orchards and woodlands. They are strong fliers and cover considerable distances during their lives. The females usually lay several batches of eggs during the early summer and migrate regularly between the fields where they lay their eggs and the woods where they feed. It is during these journeys, which are mostly undertaken at or soon after dusk, that the beetles suffer heavy casualties as they collide with cars, hitting windscreens and radiator grilles.

The harvest mouse is Britain's smallest rodent. Its diminutive size allows it to climb the cereal stalks and feed on the grains from the cereal heads.

Trees and shrubs of field and hedgerow

Some two thousand years ago about 60% of Britain was clothed with forest. Agriculture has completely transformed that primeval pattern so that nowadays over 80% is agricultural land. Contemporary woodland is found mainly in a patchwork of copses, spinneys and rough scrub, threaded together by an often ancient system of hedgerows contrived by man. Taken together, these patches and boundaries represent an important resource. Up until recently, about half the deciduous trees in the country were dispersed in hedgerows; this proportion has, however, been upset by the intrusion of Dutch elm disease. Elm had been especially favoured as a hedgerow tree in southern regions, partly because of its ability to spread by suckering. The densest suckering, at the base of the tree, also contributed to the solid framework of hedgerow, enhancing its qualities of impenetrability and shelter.

These apparently inconsequential hedgerows, therefore, along with scraps of woodland and scrub, add up to a substantial reserve of hardwood timber. However scattered, they are a vital lifeline for wildlife–undisturbed places where herbaceous plants can flower and set seed, and where animals can find food, shelter and breeding sites.

In the natural course of events, mature woodland must eventually outstrip and replace scrubland, but in our highly managed landscape man has often seen fit to retain and promote scrub for his own purposes. Thus species like hawthorn and blackthorn feature prominently in much of the patchwork, partly because they tolerate a variety of soils but more important because they provide a dense, finely branching spiny barrier against livestock.

Of outstanding consequence for wildlife is the wealth of flowering and fruiting forms which comprise the traditional shrub community. Imagine our countryside without haws, sloes and elderberries, or the riotous assembly of ivy, honeysuckle, dog rose and bramble which seethes around them. By offering tasty rewards they have enlisted animals as accomplices in their strategy to conquer new ground–showy blossoms attract pollinating insects while gaudy fruits entice birds and mammals to partake and so disperse their seeds to new pastures.

CHECKLIST

*This checklist is a guide to the trees and shrubs you will find in fields and hedgerows. Although you will not see them all in the same place, you should be able to spot many of them as you walk through the countryside during the changing seasons. The species listed in **bold** type are described in detail.*

Ash
Beech
Birch
Bird cherry
Blackthorn
Cherry-plum
Common (or English) elm
Crab apple
Dogwood
Elder
Field maple
Guelder rose
Hawthorn

Hazel
Holly
Horse chestnut
Oak
Poplar
Rowan
Spindle
Sycamore
Wayfaring tree
Whitebeam
Wild cherry (gean)
Willow
Wych elm

Above: Leaves, flowers and fruits of the hawthorn.

Left: Hawthorn is to be found in almost every hedgerow; here pink hawthorn is blooming with cow parsley.

STATELY ELMS

The English elm—in recent years much depleted by Dutch elm disease—is still in evidence, although the smaller wych elm is now more widespread.

Common or **English elm** (*Ulmus procera*) Native, deciduous, grows to 35m (110ft) in hedges, by roads. Flowers Feb, fruits May.

The Elm family (Ulmaceae) comprises 200 species of tropical and temperate trees and shrubs whose best known members are the elms. There are about 20 species of elm, and all are large deciduous trees occurring mostly in the northern hemisphere.

Elm species are difficult to distinguish from one another, but the genus can be recognised easily by two obvious leaf characteristics: one half of each leaf is always longer than the other, and each leaf has double teeth round the margins. The shoots and flowers have less distinctive but equally important features. The leaf shoots are usually arranged in fives, and each is a different shape and size; the terminal bud of most species withers, and the largest leaf comes from the second bud.

The flowers, which appear before the leaves on the previous year's twigs, occur in clusters with the male and female parts together. Each flower is small with no sepals or petals, consisting of a bell-shaped, five-lobed cup of bracts containing the reproductive parts.

The six British species growing in our fields and hedgerows are difficult to recognise because they are similar to one another and most of them hybridise. (You won't find the differences easy to recognise.) In fact, some of the 11 recorded British hybrids are better known than their parent species—it is rare to see a true species in the British countryside.

Elms are best considered in four major groups—the common or English elm, the wych elm, the smooth-leaved elms and the hybrids, the best known of which is the Dutch elm.

The common elm is considered by many people to be the unique symbol of the English countryside and is found elsewhere probably only in Brittany and south-east France. It is predominantly a native of southern England and prefers well-drained valleys in areas such as the Midlands, the Home Counties and the south-west. You rarely see it in the drier parts of eastern Kent and East Anglia where other species, notably the smooth elms, are more common.

The common elm is a beautiful domed tree which has been immortalised in Constable's 1826 painting, 'The Cornfield'. The mature tree has a massive, straight bole extending well into the crown, and a few large ascending branches. The main limbs diffuse into dense, billowing profusions of curled shoots, giving a characteristic overall dark green or blackish appearance which you do not find with other elms.

The bark is dark brown and deeply fissured, forming large, squarish plates. Suckers flourish from buds hidden beneath the bark, especially at the base of the trunk, and crowd around the middle of the tree to give a distinct skirted appearance. The common elm also produces root suckers which can grow at a surprising distance from the parent trees and even form a hedge in some cases.

Normally mature trees are stout with a long densely leafy trunk and billowing crowns representing about a third of the height. However, many trees are cropped by hedge-cutters or foresters along the trunk, giving a naked 'lollipop' shape, rather than the characteristic egg-shape.

Opposite page: English elm in full leaf. The flowers (above) appear in early spring before the leaves. The fruits are shown below.

Below: You can distinguish the wych elm by its fruits and leaf stalks: the seeds are always in the middle of the fruits, the leaf stalk is always less than 7mm ($\frac{1}{4}$in) long, and the longer part of the leaf base never overlaps the leaf stalk.

In all members of the elm family the flowers are clustered on the one-year-old twigs and appear before the leaves. They are dark red, profuse and regular. The fruits are small and rounded, each one appearing as a dry or fleshy notched membrane surrounding a single seed. Some botanists think the seeds are sterile and cannot germinate, and that the trees proliferate almost entirely from suckers. In reality the seeds lose their germinating capacity after a few days, and do not emerge through the seed coat unless they land on bare soil.

The leaves of the elm are distinctinctive. They are about 10cm (4in) long and 5cm (2in) wide, and vary in shape according to their position on the shoot. They emerge from slender, reddish brown shoots that appear in the hedgerows in April, while those on larger trees appear in May and remain on the tree until November or December.

The wych elm can be distinguished from the common by a number of characters. Wych elms are not as tall as the common elms and grow into irregular rounded shapes up to 45m (150ft) high. The lower branches start to arch from near the base of the trunk and the upper branches appear twisted, growing tortuously into the upper crown. The dull

Wych elm (*Ulmus glabra*) Native, deciduous, grows to 45m (150ft) in woods, hedgerows and beside streams. Flowers Feb, fruits May.

grey or blackish bark is smooth when young but becomes brownish-grey, fissured and ridged in mature specimens. The bark is another clue to the identity of mature trees: it appears twisted and parallel-ridged, but never deeply furrowed like that of its close relatives.

The flowers have brightly coloured stamens with crimson or purple anthers and white filaments. The leaves may be up to 16cm (6in) long, on very short stalks. They are bright green and rough above, and downy and rough on the underside.

Above: The flowers of the wych elm and (below) the fruits. The green fruits hang in conspicuous bunches in spring.

Dutch elm disease

'Dutch elm disease' is a real misnomer, since it is neither restricted to Dutch elms nor did it originate in Holland. The disease, a fungus infection affecting all elms, was discovered in France in 1818, identified in Holland in 1919, and probably originated in Asia. It was first noticed in the British Isles in 1927 and surveys showed that it was then widespread. The first outbreaks declined, and although 20% of the elms were killed, many partly diseased trees recovered, so the landscape was not damaged too much. In the late 1960s a new killer version of Dutch elm disease hit the British tree population. This epidemic has been so severe that the results have been headline news throughout the 1970s. This time the effect on the landscape has been devastating and the change irreversible. Latest Forestry Commission surveys show that more than 11 million trees have been killed out of a total estimate of $22\frac{1}{2}$ million — more than half our elms have been removed from the countryside. Interestingly, the Forestry Commission surveys have enhanced our knowledge of the distribution of the different elm groups. Disease incidence is greatest in areas with dense elm populations; wych elms and the smooth elms have escaped relatively lightly because of their sporadic distribution. The highest incidence of Dutch elm disease occurs in Sussex, Essex, the Severn-Avon valley and Hampshire, where the common elm was most widespread.

THE SYCAMORE: A WIDESPREAD ALIEN

he sycamore (below), more than any other introduced species, is widely naturalised in the British Isles. It grows in open fields, hedgerows and woods, resenting a towering and shapely mass of luxuriant foliage and a plentiful supply of seeds.

The sycamore, a native tree of central and southern Europe, especially in upland districts, was unknown in the British Isles until it was introduced in the late 15th century to ornament the estates of landowners. Since then it has been widely planted and has also spread itself vigorously. In fact no other alien tree has naturalised itself so widely in this country.

In spacious surroundings the sycamore grows into a majestic spreading tree, quite often broader than it is tall, and carrying a huge mass of foliage which by midsummer is dark green and dense. In woods it grows as tall as oaks and beeches and is quite commonly 25-30m (80-100ft) high.

Above: Sycamore blooms in profusion in early summer, its greenish flowers hanging in clusters (racemes) along the young leaves. Both sexes are present in each raceme, and you can distinguish the males by their prominent stamens.

Below: A leaf bud which is just opening in early April.

What's in a name Its name has a curious history. Originally 'sycamore' referred to a fig species, now called the sycamore-fig or mulberry fig (*Ficus sycomorus*), which grows in Palestine. When the maple-like sycamore was first brought to the British Isles from Europe it was evidently mistaken for the Holy Land 'sycamore', a well-known tree because it is mentioned in the New Testament. However, there is little resemblance between the maple-like sycamore and the mulberry-fig of Palestine, except for some similarity in leaf shape. The 'great maple', the name used in Gerard's *Herball* of 1597, is far more appropriate. The Latin name, *Acer pseudoplatanus* is also apt: it means the maple similar to the plane – in its leaf shape and shedding bark.

Spreading tree The lowest boughs may be long, slender and held out horizontally, curving slightly down about half-way along their length, but rising gracefully again near the tips. When there are no browsing animals the lower branches sweep almost to the ground, encircling the tree with a ring of foliage 30m (100ft) or more in diameter.

Above the bottom ranks of leaves are many similar layers, spaced well apart right to the top of the tree. The opposite leaves are red-stalked, toothed, up to 20cm (8in) across, and palmate with five (occasionally only three) pointed lobes. They are bright green or a deep purple-brown when they open in April.

In high summer they often become coa[ted] with honeydew.

Sycamore fruits form quickly and you [can] often find them already well developed at [the] base of the flower clusters, while new flow[ers] are still fresh at the tip. When all of the fru[it] have formed, they hang as a bunch of k[eys] which turn hard and brown in autumn.

The keys grow in pairs, each consisting [of] a seed inside a shell with a long wing attach[ed]: the two wings are almost at right angles [to] each other and slow down the fall of the see[d]: most fall directly below the parent tree [but] others become caught in the wind and d[is]persed further afield.

Like all trees of spreading habit, sycamo[re] look especially beautiful in parks and la[rge] gardens. Unfortunately because it is [ex]tremely resistant to air pollution, it of[ten] springs up in small town gardens where [it] quickly becomes a nuisance, casting too mu[ch] shade and shedding vast numbers of autu[mn] leaves which smother lawns and stop [up] drains. While some maple relatives fr[om] North America give us wonderful scarlets a[nd] yellow in autumn, the sycamore's lea[ves] achieve only a sober brown colour.

Wood The bark varies in colour from [the] grey, common on younger trees, to [the] reddish-brown of older specimens. In dar[k] western woods mature sycamores may [be] almost entirely covered by mosses, liche[ns] and polypody ferns. On old trees the ba[rk] often cracks into small plates which peel ba[ck] at the edges.

The wood of sycamore is yellowish-wh[ite] when it is in good condition. It is tough a[nd] loosely textured and is suitable for ma[ny] indoor purposes such as furniture and turn[ed] items. Cut into thin sheets it makes a go[od] veneer, especially where there is an attracti[ve] ripple mark in the grain. The wood is n[ot] durable enough however to make co[n]structural timber. Out-of-doors it r[ots] quickly and is thus useless for fencing a[nd] similar purposes.

Shelter tree Sycamore has long been valu[ed] as a quick growing, hardy shelter tree in co[ld] windy places and it has been planted on t[he] windward side of many a moorland farm[-] house. Even the salty coastal gales, fatal [to] most trees, do not kill it. In exposed sites [it] may be stunted, but still stands remarkab[ly] upright. Because of its hardiness it is a[n] especially popular tree in Scotland, where it [is] often misleadingly called the plane.

Resilient opportunist How has the sycamo[re] invade our countryside with such success? [It] is literally a species that grows pretty we[ll] anywhere, on all but the most waterlogge[d] ground. Although the best specimens occu[r] on deep, loamy soils, it grows readily on poo[r] thin soils. It is also particularly well adapte[d] to our cool, wet, windy climate.

Its fertility is remarkable: while oak an[d] beech have their good and bad years, th[e] sycamore produces a good crop of see[d]

Sycamore (*Acer pseudoplatanus*), introduced, deciduous, grows to 30m (100ft). May live up to 200 years or more. Common throughout the British Isles in open fields, woods, hedges, parks, gardens and city streets. Very tolerant of exposure and salt spray and often planted as a shelter tree. Regenerates itself easily in most soils. Flowers and fruits, April-June or July.

ractically every year of its long life of up to 00 years, (and some authorities say many 1ore,) and the seeds are dispersed efficiently.

In spring the seedlings germinate readily, eventually forming small thickets in open round such as the site of a felled wood. 3ecause sycamore is an aggressive pioneering pecies, pure oakwood can eventually become eplaced by pure sycamore wood. After Vorld War II crowds of young sycamores uickly invaded bomb sites in many cities.

In the British Isles, perhaps because it is so ar from its natural place in the world, it uffers from comparatively few insect pests. Neighbouring oaks can be severely attacked y caterpillars while sycamores are hardly ouched. Only in real plague years do aterpillars spill over from oaks to sycamore eaves.

Very few moths prefer to eat sycamores: here is one species called the sycamore moth, ut it is not a pest species. The best-known ungus on sycamore is the tar-spot which proluces innumerable black blotches on the eaves, yet it is not a threat to the tree's health. t is rare in industrial areas because it is kept t bay by the sulphur dioxide in the air.

Nature conservationists have ambivalent eelings about the sycamore. They dislike the vay its deep shade suppresses the plants and 1ence much of the animal life below it. They ire not happy to see it occupying ground vhich would otherwise be occupied by oak, oirch or other trees more attractive to cateroillars and birds.

On the other hand there are points in favour of the sycamore. Its reliable seed production s welcomed by wildlife in years when acorns and beech mast fail. Its flaking bark harbours many small creatures which are sought by winter birds. Bees and other insects swarm to the flowers in spring, and its heavy leaf fall contributes greatly to woodland litter. And it provides a reliable shelter for wildlife in exposed areas.

Above: Sycamore fruits hang in paired keys (samaras), each of which contains a single seed. When the samara reaches the ground the fruit case does not split open, but slowly decays, allowing the seed to germinate the following spring.

Right: Sycamore seedlings grow easily and fast—up to 50cm (20in) a year in the early stages.

MAPLES: GLOWING AUTUMN GOLD

The field maple is our only native maple species and it is rather a small tree; but what it lacks in size it more than makes up for by the brilliance of its fine autumn foliage which turns to vivid shades of golden yellow.

The field maple usually grows in hedgerow either as a small tree with a neat rounde crown, or chopped right back to a bush form ing part of the hedge itself. It is also foun among hillside scrub, at the edges of wood and in the shrub layer of oakwoods where i the past it was usually coppiced. It grow best on chalk and limestone soils and is thu widespread in southern and eastern Englan but less common in western and norther districts. In Scotland and Ireland it has bee introduced and has a rather scanty distribu tion.

Britain's native maple The trunk is covere with pale greyish-brown bark which, i older trees, is cracked by a network o

sures. The winter twigs are light brown and ~~ored~~ along their length by shallow furrows. ~~lder~~ twigs tend to develop prominent ~~ngitudinal~~ ridges of corky bark. The small ~~own~~ buds are carried in opposite pairs ~~ong~~ the length of the twig, and they break ~~en~~ in early May to release the young leaves.

The fresh young leaves hang limp and are ~~le~~ yellow-green with a coating of fine ~~irs~~. Their upper surface has a noticeably ~~ossy~~ sheen. Later, as the leaves expand, they ~~iffen~~ and turn a darker shade of green. The ~~af~~-blade is divided into three or five distinct ~~bes~~ which are separated by deep indenta-~~ons~~. Each lobe has bluntly toothed edges ~~id~~ a rounded tip.

Leaf size can vary enormously: the leaves ~~n~~ a regularly trimmed hedge are generally ~~>out~~ half the size of those on free-growing ~~ees~~. The leaves are borne on leaf-stalks ~~-8cm~~ (1½-3in) long which are light green or ~~reaked~~ with red. If you cut the leaf stalk it ~~leeds~~ a white milky sap.

The field maple flowers shortly after the ~~>liage~~ has unfurled. A loose cluster of ~~)-20~~ greenish-yellow flowers is supported ~~n~~ a stalk that grows upwards between the ~~rminal~~ pair of leaves on each twig. Each ~~ower~~ has five green petals surrounding ~~ight~~ stamens, which are tipped with yellow ~~ollen~~-bearing anthers.

Insects, and particularly bees, feed on ~~ie~~ pollen and nectar and as they do so they ~~ansfer~~ pollen from the male anthers to the ~~entral~~ female style. The style is situated ~~t~~ the top of the ovary which is made up of ~~vo~~ green flattened lobes. After fertilisation ~~ne~~ ovary develops rapidly into a pair of ~~road~~-winged keys (samaras). They hang in ~~unches~~ throughout summer, slowly chang-~~ng~~ colour from a crimson-tinged green to

Field maple *(Acer campestre)*.
Deciduous, native, grows to 26m (85ft) in woodland, hedgerows and scrubland mainly in southern England, rare elsewhere. Flowers May-June.

Below: The fruits of the field maple are set in a straight line: those of the sycamore, our most common maple species, are set at an angle.

Opposite page and below: The brilliant autumn colours displayed by maples result from the unusually high concentration of sugar in the leaves and the sap. (Maple syrup is made from the sap of Norway maple.)

brown by autumn. When the seeds fall from the tree the wing gives them a spinning motion.

Timber Field maple wood burns well but because of the meagre size of the tree it has never been widely used. The pale brown timber has a well marked grain which is still valued by craftsmen. The wood from the roots, with its beautiful swirling pattern of veins, shows up well when polished.

Sycamore look-alike Field maple can be confused at first with the sycamore, but there are several differences: the sycamore's winter twigs are smooth, with yellow-green buds; sycamore leaves, although similar in shape, are larger than those of the field maple, and the lobes more pointed and not so widely separated; also the samaras of the field maple have broader wings set in a straight line, whereas sycamore samaras are joined at an angle of about 55 degrees.

Sugary sap The sap of all maple species is especially rich in sugars. When growth surges ahead in spring there is a great flow of sugars from the winter storage organs to fuel the development of shoots and leaves. In northern Europe the sap was collected in cups set under hollow tubes driven into the trunk. The liquid was boiled over a fire to concentrate it into a thick sweet syrup. Nowadays the main source of maple syrup comes from the sugar maple (*A. saccharum*) which is widespread in much of the deciduous woodland of north America.

GLISTENING WHITEBEAM

Anyone who walks the steep slopes of the South Downs in high summer will recognise the distinctive foliage of the whitebeam tree. This compact species shimmers from green to silver as the leaves turn with the wind.

In the wild the whitebeam is found chiefly on the chalk of central, south and south eastern England. One of its main strongholds is the Chilterns where it grows amid scrub thickets, in open woods and clearings and along hedgerows. The tree is also scattered in limestone districts elsewhere and is often planted in parks and gardens and along city streets because it is tolerant of shade and pollution.

Appearance The smooth brown twigs bear large, oval, greenish buds which break into leaf in late April. A striking feature of this tree is that when the young leaves emerge they grow vertically from the bud, irrespective of the angle of the twig, and are held stiffly up before unfolding. Th

in marked contrast to most native trees in
which the young leaves at first hang limply
from the open buds. The whiteness of the
underside of the leaves comes from their coat
of felty hairs which help to check water loss—a
useful feature on the dry limestone soils on
which the tree grows.

The expanded leaves, 5-12cm (2-5in) long,
are oval in shape and borne on short stalks.
The upper surface is darkish green and the
underside is densely felted with white hairs
that give the foliage its silvery appearance.

The blossom follows in May or June. The
white, five-petalled flowers, each about 1.5cm
(1in) across, are clustered in loose bunches
on green stalks which, like the leaves, are
clothed in fine white hairs. Insect visitors,
and especially flies, are responsible for
pollination. The fruits which are up to 1.5cm
(1in) long, ripen by October to a rich shiny
scarlet and hang heavily from the twigs. Each
fruit contains two hard seeds which are widely
dispersed in the droppings of birds that feed
on the bright red berries. The berries are
also eaten by squirrels, hedgehogs and voles.

In Lancashire and Cumbria the berries are
called chess-apples. The flesh is yellow and
the young berries have a rough, sharp taste,
but the flavour is said to improve slightly
with age. Although not poisonous to man, the
berries are not recommended eating.

The wood is hard and pale yellow, but the
tree seldom provides a useful volume of
timber so has only been used for items turned
on lathes; it also makes useful firewood.

Hybrids The whitebeam is tremendously
variable. The name *Sorbus aria* is one that
encompasses a large group of microspecies
which differ slightly in flower form and in the
size and shape of the leaves and berries. Some
of these come about as a result of hybrid-
ation with other native *Sorbus* species.

Commonly planted hybrids of *Sorbus*
species include the bastard service tree which
is a cross between rowan and the service tree
of Fontainebleau. The service tree of Fontainebleau is itself a hybrid of whitebeam and
the wild service tree. The bastard service tree
is a fairly common tree of city streets and
parks.

Above: **Whitebeam** *(Sorbus aria)*, native, deciduous, grows to 20m (65ft), mainly on chalk and limestone soils in southern England. Flowers May-June, fruits Sept.

Above: Whitebeam gets its name from the white underside of the leaves. It can be distinguished from other species of *Sorbus* such as rowan because the leaves are undivided.

Left and below: The flowers and fruits of the whitebeam make the tree particularly handsome in summer and autumn.

BLACKTHORN AND CHERRY-PLUM

Blackthorn and cherry-plum may look alike at a quick first glance. But look closer, and you'll see that blackthorn is a prickly, rigid bush with tangled branches, whereas cherry-plum is an elegant tree with smooth bark and larger leaves and flowers.

Left: A close-up view of blackthorn in full blossom. The pure white, starry flowers are attractive to quite a variety of insects.

Below: Blackthorn breaks into a mass of blossom in spring, before the leaves appear.

The blackthorn is a deciduous shrub which is one of the best protected against grazing animals: it positively bristles with stiff, spiny thorns on the twigs, branches and even the stem. It is common throughout the British Isles on most types of soil and in a wide variety of habitats. It is most conspicuous on scrublands where it forms dense, impenetrable thickets, but rarely grows taller than 4m (13ft), and on windswept coastal cliffs it is shaped and stunted by the prevailing winds.

Blackthorn also grows in woodland but because it needs plenty of light you are unlikely to see it in the shady interior, although it thrives on the edges of woods and in clearings, along road verges, grassy tracks, hedgerows, embankments, and on commons.

The blackthorn is a rigid bush, sending out many branches which further divide to form a close network of twigs, each ending in a sharp point. The bark is usually quite smooth and blackish—hence the name—but the younger shoots are covered with fine downy hairs. The older branches are frequently thickly encrusted with lichens.

Prickly trap It is not surprising that many birds choose to nest in blackthorn bushes, their eggs and nestlings relatively secure from predators by being tucked away in their spiny fortress. The most important is the red-backed shrike, a rather rare bird which has an interesting habit of impaling its prey on to the tips of thorns. The shrike's 'larder' is a store of surplus food which is either eaten later or fed to the young.

The blackthorn's tight prickly growth would seem to make it an ideal hedging plant

Above: Sloes are hard to
collect because blackthorn
bushes are so prickly, but
added to gin, they make a
delicious drink.

Right: **Blackthorn** (*Prunus
spinosa*). Deciduous, native,
grows to 4m (13ft) in scrub,
woods, hedges. Flowers
April, sloes Aug-Sept.

Below: The remains of a
lizard impaled on black-
thorn. Beetles, frogs, bees
and nestlings are also stored
in this way and eaten
by the red-backed shrike.

for creating stockproof barriers. Indeed it i
but there is one drawback: blackthorn send
up erect shoots or suckers from its roots, ofte
several feet from the main stem. If these a
not cut back they gradually spread out int
the pasture, eventually forming a dense thick
that is difficult to remove. This suckerin
habit means that a large clump of blackthorn
can result from just one plant spreadin
vegetatively.

Flowers The blackthorn flowers early,
March or April, before the foliage appear
Each flower is composed of five pure whi
petals, and they are pollinated by insects.
some years the starry blossoms cover th
twigs in such profusion that you can hard
see the bark.

Many people believe that if the weather
cold when blackthorn blossom appears the
it will remain cold for the whole flowerin
period – about a fortnight – a so-called black
thorn winter. It is easy to dismiss these ag
old beliefs, but there was a typical blackthor
winter in 1981: a week of below-averag
temperatures in mid-April culminated i
blizzards which swept across most of th
country, cutting off farms and villages an
causing chaos on the roads. The fact is tha
the flowering of blackthorn does often co
incide with a cold winter.

Leaves The leaf buds are spaced alternatel
along the twigs and the foliage unfurls i
May. The leaves are small, about 3cm (1 in
long, oval in shape with finely toothe
margins. A large number of moth caterpillar
feed on the leaves, as do the caterpillars o
two small butterflies, the brown hairstreak
and the rare black hairstreak, which is know
only in a few places in the Midlands. Afte
mating the females of both species lay thei
eggs on blackthorn twigs where they pass th
winter before hatching early the following
summer.

Sloes The flowers are succeeded by har
green fruits which ripen and swell during
summer to become the familiar small, round
blackish plums called sloes. Each one is abou
15mm ($\frac{1}{2}$in) across and the black skin i
usually coated with a dusty bloom which
gives them a bluish-grey colour. A singl
round stone is embedded within the greenish-
yellow flesh.

Sloes are extremely sour and if you bit
into one it will set your teeth on edge. However those fruits that linger on the bush for
month or so do become slightly sweeter
Sloes can be used with sugar for making
wine or steeped in gin to produce sloe-gin,
an excellent liqueur-type drink.

Blackthorn wood is hard and the grain forms
intricate patterns of colour. The straight
stems from younger bushes make handsome
walking sticks. In Ireland the shillelagh, a
fearsome cudgel traditionally carried for
personal protection, is usually fashioned
from blackthorn. Shillelaghs are still made
today for sale as tourist souvenirs.

The **cherry-plum** or myrobalan is a small deciduous tree growing to about 8m (26ft) in height. The trunk, which is covered with smooth blackish bark, sends out slender branches to form a rather narrow, rounded crown. As a young bush it can easily be confused with blackthorn but the twigs are much less thorny and the leaves are generally larger – up to 7cms (3in) long.

The cherry-plum is native to Asia Minor and it is not known for certain when it was introduced to the British Isles, but it was recorded growing here in the 16th century. It has a rather local distribution, more or less limited to south and eastern regions of England. In some districts it was widely used as a hedge plant, for it tolerates heavy cutting and does not sucker freely like the blackthorn, so is easier to control and maintain. It is also locally planted in shelterbelts around orchards but elsewhere it grows wild in overgrown hedgerows and waysides. The white flowers are a larger version of blackthorn blossom, about 2cm ($\frac{3}{4}$in) across, but not produced in such quantity. The flowers appear in April, before the leaves unfold, but they are easily damaged by frost and so rarely produce much fruit in the British Isles. In September, if the spring has been mild, the tree becomes laden with reddish 'cherry-plums' each about 2.5cms (1in) in diameter and hanging from a 2cm ($\frac{3}{4}$in) long stalk. They are delicious to eat.

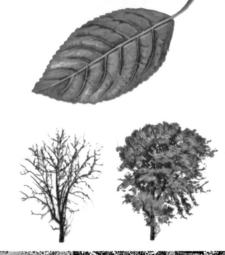

Above and below: Cherry-plum is usually planted along hedgerows although it is occasionally naturalised. It is widely believed that an ancient hybrid between blackthorn and cherry-plum gave rise to all our domestic plum trees including bullaces, damsons and greengages.

Left: **Cherry-plum** (*Prunus cerasifera*). Deciduous, introduced, grows to 8m (26ft) in hedgerows. Flowers March, only fruits in good years.

MAY IN BLOOM SAYS SUMMER IS HERE

Of all our native trees, the common hawthorn has contributed most to the patchwork appearance of the British rural landscape. It forms dense thorny hedges and thickets, teeming with wildlife, and its glorious bloom in May proclaims the oncoming summer.

Far left: Hawthorn in bloom in May. An old country rhyme recommends the tree as protection for man and beast in thunderstorms:
Beware the oak—
it courts the stroke.
Beware the ash—
it courts the flash.
Creep under the thorn—
it will save you from harm.

Right: The pink anthers of hawthorn shrivel and turn brown after shedding their pollen.

There are two species of hawthorn in the British Isles, the common hawthorn and the Midland hawthorn. The common hawthorn is abundant throughout the country, except in the far north of Scotland. It thrives on most soils, in open habitats such as hillsides, neglected pastures, on commons and in woodland and most hedgerows. Left to itself it grows in dense thickets and forms a distinct habitat during the natural transformation of grassland into woodland. In open, exposed places, especially around the coast, its growth becomes stunted and shaped by the strong prevailing winds.

The Midland hawthorn is not nearly so widespread and is more or less confined to the East Midlands and south-east England, where you often find it in the shrub layer of oak woods. You can distinguish between the two species by looking at the leaves and flowers.

The leaves of the common hawthorn have distinct lobes and indentations that may reach as far as the midrib. The tips of the lobes tend to be serrated, and the whole leaf is longer than it is broad. The leaves of the Midland hawthorn are more rounded in outline, with small lobes and shallow indentations, and are broader than they are long. The leaves of both hawthorns have a nutty flavour; they used to be eaten by children and were often called 'bread and cheese'. The foliage is devoured by huge numbers of insects, especially the caterpillars of various moths such as the winter and the burnished brass. In autumn the leaves turn in colour to rich tints of red, orange and yellow before the wind and frost strip the branches bare.

Blossom Hawthorn blossoms in May—hence the familiar name, May—shortly after the leaves have unfurled. The trees soon become smothered in clusters of white, and occasionally pale pink, flowers. (Some of the crimson and double-flowered varieties that are common in city streets have been introduced.) Common hawthorn flowers have only one style (female part) and seed which develops later inside the red berry. Midland hawthorn flowers have two or occasionally three styles and seeds. Often the two species hybridise and then both types of flower

Common hawthorn (*Crataegus monogyna*). Deciduous, native, grows as a hedge or a shrub; may reach 10m (40ft) as a tree. Found in woodland and scrub. Fruits Sept.

The hawthorn's strong spines, which are really modified branches, make the tree impenetrable to grazing animals, and for this reason it is commonly planted for hedges.

appear on the same tree. The hybrids are fertile.

The berries, known as haws, start to turn red in late August and provide a rich splash of colour along wayside hedgerows well into autumn. However it is not unusual to find bunches of berries which appear not to have ripened at all; these remain yellow-green.

Haws last well into winter and are a vital source of food for birds, especially during cold spells. Blackbirds, thrushes and large flocks of redwings and fieldfares – winter visitors from northern Europe – are just a few of the species that can be seen along hedgerows, settling to pluck the berries from their stalks.

Right: A dormouse tucking in to ripe haws. The carbohydrate in the flesh of the berries helps the animal to fatten up for winter hibernation.

Below: Hawthorn bearing typical red berries in autumn in Yorkshire. This species is one of the first colonizers of scrubland and uncultivated areas.

Birds are essential to the spread of ha thorns. The seeds, embodied in the berri flesh, have a tough coat which prevents pip being digested by the birds which even ally drop them some distance from the par tree.

Living fences Common hawthorn has be used for about 2000 years as natural barb fencing. Its tangle of thorny branches is ideal barrier for enclosing livestock. Inde the Anglo-Saxon word is *haegthorn*, wh means hedge-tree. Signs of defensive ha thorn hedges have been found round the e of excavated Roman forts. Evidently th function was to keep out marauding nat warriors bent on driving the occupying ar from their homeland.

During the last 300 years hundreds of mi of hawthorn hedge were planted as an alt native to stone walls, ditches or hurdles. this century they have increasingly be grubbed out or replaced by fencing that quires less maintenance.

Trees Unmolested by hedge-cutters, ha thorns grow into medium-sized trees w dense, rounded crowns. They live for a su prisingly long time: their natural span usually around 100 years but specimens th have reached the ripe old age of 300 are n uncommon. In old age the trunks becon gnarled, twisted and furrowed. Consta rubbing by cattle tends to polish the ba leaving it with rather a glossy sheen. The tre slow growth produces very hard wood. Ha thorn logs burn well, but curiously this tou timber is otherwise little used, except o casionally for tool-handles and walki sticks.

May Day During the celebrations of t arrival of summer, maypoles were erected village greens and in town squares ar decorated with garlands of May blosso However it is traditionally thought to unlucky to bring sprigs of flowering hawtho indoors. Superstition holds that it may resu in a death in the family.

Quite recently it was discovered that one the chemicals that make up the flower sweet scent is also produced during the dec of corpses. Small wonder, then, that peop were reluctant to bring the 'smell of deat into their homes. It seems likely that th superstition dates back to outbreaks of th Great Plague when so many dead lay un buried.

Legendary thorn The most famous haw thorn in England is the Glastonbury thorn One legend surrounding this unusual tre goes back to the time when that part Somerset called Avalon was surrounded b sea. Joseph of Arimathea was supposed t have landed there during his pilgrimage fron the Holy Lands of Palestine. Resting afte climbing a particularly steep hill, Josep thrust his thorn staff into the ground where i miraculously took root and flowered im mediately.

THE WANDERING WAYFARING TREE

From spring through to late autumn the wayfaring tree adorns the roadsides of southern Britain. Heads of white flowers in May are soon followed by bright red berries. With the arrival of autumn the berries have turned a glossy black and the leaves are turning shades of red to provide a final touch of colour.

Below: A wayfaring tree (*Viburnum lantana*) in flower. Its requirement for a dry, well-drained and preferably alkaline soil limits its distribution in the British Isles: it is common only in southern England (except the West Country) and the south Midlands. On the Continent, however, it is a common shrub throughout central and southern Europe, and extends into north Africa and western Asia.

The name 'wayfaring' tree seems an appropriate choice for this roadside plant, yet it arose through a misunderstanding. The Latin name, 'viburnum', gave rise to the French word for the wayfaring tree, 'viorne'. This was mistakenly thought by the 16th century herbalist, Gerard, to derive from the Latin word 'via', meaning a road. So he named it the wayfarer's tree—it seemed to him a suitable name because he encountered it frequently on his journeys between London and Canterbury. The name 'wayfaring' tree has stuck ever since.

The wayfaring tree grows best on chalk or limestone soils, such as those found between London and Canterbury, but it is occasionally seen growing elsewhere provided the soil is dry and well drained. It is most common in the southern counties of England and the south Midlands, although it is absent from the West Country and parts of East Anglia. In Wales it is native to a narrow strip along the south coast. It is not thought to be native to areas north of Yorkshire, although it has been introduced to Scotland, particularly in the lowlands. It is, however, entirely absent from the Scottish islands and the Isle of Man. In Ireland the wayfaring tree is not native but it has been introduced to a few places.

Woods and hedgerows are the most likely habitats in which to find a wayfaring tree. It sometimes forms small, rather open thickets and can produce suckers which, given the chance, rapidly invade grassland and other open habitats close by.

Sizeable shrub Despite its common name the wayfaring tree rarely grows into a tree. It almost always remains a shrub, though sometimes a substantial one reaching a height of 6m (20ft). It has a regular branching pattern and its buds are borne naked on the shoots—that is, the buds have no protective scales to cover the undeveloped leaves. Instead they are insulated from the frost and cold weather of winter by a coating of hairs, giving the buds a greyish, felted look. The presence of naked buds on the shoot distinguishes the wayfaring tree from the other members of its genus, *Viburnum*.

The leaves are borne in opposite pairs on the shoots. They have a rather wrinkled appearance and are oval or slightly heart-shaped with finely toothed margins. They may reach a length of 10cm (4in). The upper surfaces of the leaves, and the young twigs, are covered with the same greyish hairs found on the buds. The lower surfaces of the leaves are also covered with hairs, but here they are much thicker and woollier in appearance. While the hairs on the buds are there to provide protection against the winter, the hairs on the leaves clearly perform a quite different function because the leaves are shed in the autumn. The purpose of these is to prevent the leaves from losing too much moisture in the dry habitats that the wayfaring tree often prefers.

Stems for withies The distinctive white

Right: A flowering head of a wayfaring tree. All the flowers are similar to each other—unlike another species of *Viburnum*, the guelder rose, in which the flowers on the outside of the head are much larger than those on the inside. Each flower is about 5mm across and contains five white petals fused together. Inside this tube are five conspicuous yellow stamens. The flowers of the closely related elder have the same structure.

Above: Young berries of a wayfaring tree. The berries start off green but soon turn a bright red (right) before becoming a shiny black in early autumn. Each berry is about 8mm long and oval with a fleshy interior, inside which are embedded several seeds. The berries have too sharp a taste for humans but they are a popular source of food for birds, which devour them eagerly and so disperse the seeds. The juice from the berries was once used to make black ink.

woolly undersides of the wayfaring tree's leaves have given rise to many alternative names for this tree, such as mealytree, cottontree, whitewood and hoarwithy. The last of these colloquial names also refers to the use of the supple young stems for binding and tying things together, a withy being any stem or twig flexible enough to be used for these purposes. Withies from the wayfaring tree were used to tie up bundles of faggots and as hoops for fastening gates. They also provided switches (small tapered rods) for driving cattle, and handles for whips, from which come two other colloquial names for the wayfaring tree–twistwood and whipcrop.

Elder-like flowers The wayfaring tree flowers in May and June, each shrub producing numerous tiny white-petalled flowers borne in large umbel-like clusters up to 10cm (4in) across. Superficially the flower heads resemble those of an elder bush–the two species belong to the same family, the honeysuckle family–but the elder flowers slightly later in the year, usually in June and July.

In July the flowers are followed by fleshy oval berries, again resembling those of elder. The berries of a wayfaring tree are green when young but soon become bright red and eventually turn black and shiny when fully ripe in about September. The berries are not poisonous but they have an extremely tart taste and are not recommended for eating.

As the year advances the wayfaring tree becomes even more colourful and the leaves take on their autumn hues of red, providing a striking contrast to the clusters of shiny black berries.

Close relative Another member of the same genus–*Viburnum*–is sometimes found growing in the wild. This is the laurustinus, a species that, though not native to the British Isles, has become naturalised here in some areas.

The laurustinus is native to the Mediterranean region, particularly southern Italy and north Africa. It was first introduced to Britain during the 16th century and has been cultivated in gardens ever since, sometimes escaping to the wild.

Like the wayfaring tree, the laurustinus is a shrub, though smaller–usually between 2m (6ft) and 4m (13ft) high–and with a domed crown. It differs from the wayfaring tree in being evergreen, as its thick, leathery, dark green leaves suggest. It bears a great many branches from ground level upwards.

The flowers of the two species are similar, except that the outsides of the laurustinus petals may be tinged pink. Also, the flower heads are often smaller on laurustinus, usually 5-10cm (2-4in) across, and they appear at a quite different time of the year, opening in November and often continuing to flower through the winter until April, depending on the severity of the weather.

Although laurustinus flowers prolifically in Britain, it rarely produces fruits here. When they do appear, however, they are smaller than the fruits of the wayfaring tree, and a striking metallic blue in colour. Nevertheless, the fact that laurustinus occasionally sets fruit in Britain has allowed it to escape from gardens and establish itself in the wild.

Different specimens of laurustinus can be very variable in such features as leaf shape, size of flower head and so forth. This suggests that there are a number of different races in this species that have become adapted to different climates. Some, for example, are adapted to the warmth of the Mediterranean while others–presumably those that set fruit here–are adapted to the cooler, moister climate of Britain.

Above: The elder acts as an astringent (a binding agent) to mammalian digestive systems and is avoided by herbivores. Hence the plant is likely to be the survivor in places where most or all of the other more palatable herbage is stripped bare. For humans, the unpleasant smell of a sprig of elder keeps flies at bay. In the past the leaves were dried and used as an insecticide.

THE ELDER: PRIZED FOR ITS BERRIES

Elder flowers and berries have long been used by man in wine making. Birds, too, feast on the berries, but both man and animals avoid the ill-smelling leaves.

The elder is one of our most common woo plants. It is more frequently seen as a shr but it can grow to a tree as high as 10m (33f It grows almost everywhere, from heav polluted roadsides to wind-lashed cliff-to where it is crusted with salt from the sea spra It thrives on waste ground, in hedgerows, heathland, chalk downs, woodland and scr and especially where the soil is rich in nitr gen from the manure of animals such as ra bits and badgers. You often see it near drai and sewers–it can be a sign to archaeologi of the site of former dwellings.

Leaves, appearing on the elder in sprin are dark green, toothed and lance-shape They have a particularly unpleasant sme ther like that of a neglected mouse cage, d, like the flowers, seem to have little traction for most insects, which shun them.

Flowers The elder is an impressive sight hen its stout branches are laden with flat-pped clusters (corymbs) of creamy yellow wers. They can be up to 20cm (8in) in ameter, and they emit a heady fragrance nich was once thought to be poisonous. The wers are mainly pollinated by small flies, at occasionally hoverflies or bees land on the wers and collect pollen from the pale yel-w anthers. The species is usually cross-llinated.

The berries are small and green at first, but ey ripen to a deep purple colour in August. early September the branches have be-me so heavy under the weight of their load at the berries sag on limp, claret-coloured ems. The berries, like the flowers, were once ought to be poisonous. Nowadays we make em into elderberry wine, chutney, jelly and tchup. The taste of the fruit can be cloying human palates, but large numbers of rds such as blackbirds, pigeons, rooks, arlings, robins and blackcaps relish the uits.

Seed dispersal The elder is widely dispersed birds swallowing the fruits and excreting e small hard seeds. Small shrubberies spring around tree trunks where starlings have osted above.

Elder saplings grow particularly quickly– to a metre (3ft) in their first season. The ice of this rapid growth is that the stems e weak and pithy; the tree is easily damaged d after a gale the bushes become a tangle of oken boughs. The tree also spreads itself means of suckers which can sprout some stance from the parent tree.

Wood The bark of elder is brownish-grey, eply furrowed, corky and with very pro-inent lenticels (pore-like openings) through hich the stems breathe. Pieces of the thinner ranches are often hollowed out by children the country to make pea-shooters and histles.

The name elder is derived from the Anglo-axon *eldrum*, meaning fire–perhaps a refer-ice to the time before the invention of ellows when the hollowed branches were sed for blowing on fires. The mature wood hard and sometimes used to make small ticles like toys.

Elder wood seems to be defenceless against tacks of fungi. The most common is the w's ear fungus, which also thrives on the ead branches. Honey agaric and oyster ngi are also common parasites.

Elder uses The flowers and berries have ng been used to make wine. The flowers add distinctive flavour to stewed fruit, and elder-ower water is still sold as a mild skin clean-r. The berries are rich in vitamin C. A dark ky dye used to be made from the berries, and reen dye from the leaves. Like many trees, der was supposed to have magic powers.

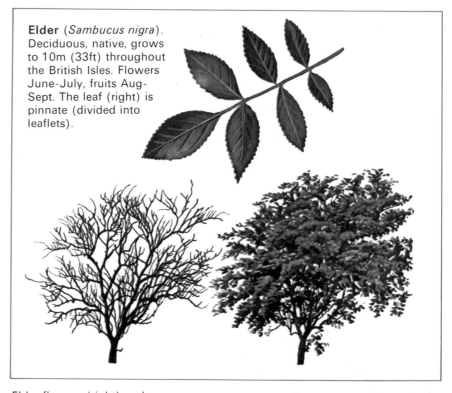

Elder (*Sambucus nigra*). Deciduous, native, grows to 10m (33ft) throughout the British Isles. Flowers June-July, fruits Aug-Sept. The leaf (right) is pinnate (divided into leaflets).

Elder flowers (right) and berries (below) have their culinary uses, but the tree itself has long been credited with supernatural powers. Invaders from northern Europe who settled here after the Roman occupation are said to have planted elders among the rotting bodies of executed criminals, hoping the plant would absorb their badness and so bring peace to their souls.

Flowers and fruits of field and hedgerow

The mixed ancestry of our much-fragmented countryside is nowhere more apparent than in the community of flowering plants and grasses which inherits it today. Flowers that carpeted meadows in a time when agriculture was less intensive have claimed the sanctuary of field edges, hedgebanks and roadsides, gilding the seams of a rural patchwork. Relect swards of chalk downland, rich in colourful herbs and vetches, are cast like so many coral atolls in a sea of arable farming. But while survivors like these of a less disturbed landscape have lost ground, others have profited: many species that were once engulfed in the canopied gloom of extensive deciduous woodland have multiplied quickly in the sunnier, more open aspect created by forest clearance, often achieving a vigour and luxuriance that deep shade had denied them.

Because our climate is so highly seasonal, the plant community also undergoes profound changes within the span of a single year. The long, colourless days of winter generate a growing sense of anticipation in the waysides as February creeps into March. With the quickening of spring, hardy shoots of rosebay willowherb, lords-and-ladies and cow parsley are the first to break cover. But, on a south-facing bank, the lesser celandine's lustrous yellow stars are often the first heralds of the plant kingdom's approaching summer. By May pioneer celandines and primroses are fast disappearing under a welter of nettles, garlic mustard, woundwort and other challengers for light and space. There is also growing competition for the pollinating favours of flying insects, especially bees and butterflies.

On chalk downland, however, many plants have foregone the race for light which would unduly expose them to the destructive grazing pressures of herbivores such as sheep and rabbits. Instead they develop as flattened rosettes bearing a profusion of flowers which, in the soft breeze of a July day, fill the air with an unmistakable downland fragrance. Chalk and limestone soils also favour an elite group of plants which are perhaps the most dramatic in our flora; these are the orchids, of which Britain has 49 species. Though some, like the pyramidal orchid, may occur in great profusion, many others are extremely rare.

CHECKLIST

This checklist is a guide to the flowers and grasses you will find in fields and hedgerows. Although you will not see them all in the same place, you should be able to spot many of them as you walk through the countryside during the changing seasons. The species listed in **bold** *type are described in detail.*

Bird's-foot trefoil
Black bryony
Bramble
Burdock
Chalk milkwort
Cock's-foot grass
Coltsfoot
Cow parsley
Cowslip
Dandelion
Dog rose
Early purple orchid
Foxglove
Garlic mustard
Germander speedwell
Greater knapweed
Hedgerow crane's-bill
Herb robert
Hogweed
Horseshoe vetch
Lady's bedstraw

Lesser celandine
Lords-and-ladies
Meadow buttercup
Meadowsweet
Nettle
Ox-eye daisy
Primrose
Purple loosestrife
Pyramidal orchid
Quaking grass
Red campion
Red clover
Rosebay willowherb
Sheep's fescue
Sorrel
Spear thistle
Sweet violet
Teasel
Wild thyme
Woody nightshade
Yellow rattle

Above: Spring cinquefoil flowers among rocky grassland.

Left: In summer our waysides and field edges are ablaze with colour from a profusion of wild flowers and grasses.

69

DOG ROSE–EMBLEM OF ENGLAND

The simple but beautiful dog rose (below), which can be seen scrambling over hedgerows throughout the country (with the exception of the far north), is the most common wild rose in Britain and a forerunner of many exotic garden varieties.

The dog rose is by far the most common of o[ur] wild roses. It grows extensively in hedgerow[s] thickets and scrub throughout the Briti[sh] Isles, except in the far north of Scotland. [It] seems to achieve its best growth along wil[d] straggling hedgerows that have escaped cu[t]ting for many years. Using these hedges f[or] support as it climbs, the dog rose displays [a] bright cascade of large flowers in summer.

The dog rose possesses a large woo[dy] rootstock from which arise the long, archi[ng] stems armed with broad, sharp prickl[es] shaped like shark fins. The stems grow up [to] three metres (10ft) long and if they are c[ut] down to their base they are replaced by ne[w] shoots, or suckers which spring from t[he]

70

nderground rootstock.

The formidable prickles deter grazing animals and help the plant to keep a firm hold on ...e bushes over which it clambers and ...rawls. You can test their effectiveness by ...ying to pull a stem (you will have to wear ...oves) away from the bush over which it is ...aped. It is surprisingly difficult and some...mes impossible without enlisting the help ... other people.

The flowers are faintly scented, and are ...orne singly or in groups of three or four on ...de branches towards the end of each stem. ...he blooms have five slightly notched petals ...hich are usually white with rims tinged with ...elicate pink, although pure white or pure ...ink flowers do occur.

Set around the middle of the flower are ...usters of numerous bright yellow stamens ...rrounding the central stalked style. The ...yle (female part) provides a channel along ...hich pollen grains travel down to the ovary ... fertilise the eggs. The ovary is enclosed ...ithin the green bulb upon which the flower ...sts. After fertilisation these fleshy recept...les change into shiny red, flask-shaped ...ips, which are a characteristic and colourful ...ature of the countryside in autumn.

The fruits last well into winter and, because ...ey tend not to mature all at the same time, ...og rose bushes bear a mixture of ripe and ...pening hips. The mature scarlet hips are ...ought by birds, especially blackbirds, field...res and wood pigeons, and the seeds are ...ispersed in their droppings. Those that are ...ot eaten by birds eventually fall to the ground ...nd provide food for mammals such as voles ...nd badgers.

The foliage which emerges in April is a ...resh bright green, but during summer the ...eaves darken somewhat and acquire a glossy ...urface sheen. Each leaf stalk has a number of

hips

prickles

Below: The sweet perfume of wild rose buds soon disappears once the flowers have fully opened.

Above: Rose hips are a valuable source of vitamin C. During World War II when the disruption to shipping created severe shortages of citrus fruits, hips were collected on a large scale to make rose-hip syrup which was given to pregnant women and young children.

Left: **Dog rose** *(Rosa canina).* Native shrub growing to 3m (10ft) in woods and hedgerows. Rare in Scotland. Flowers June-July, fruits Aug onwards.

prickles on its underside and carries from five to seven leaflets with a sharply toothed margin.

If you examine the leaves of dog roses—or garden roses for that matter—you may notice neat oval or semi-circular gaps in the leaflets which look as though someone has attacked the bush with a hole-puncher. This is the remarkable handiwork of leaf-cutting bees, nine species of which live in Britain.

Modern garden roses have a complex ancestry because there has been much cross-breeding between the different species. The first roses with double blooms date to Roman times and originated when unusual hybrids of wild species were preserved and subsequently cultivated. Nowadays the dog rose plays an important role in commercial rose growing, providing the rootstocks on to which exotic blooming varieties are frequently grafted.

The name dog rose is sometimes said to originate from Roman times when a soldier was bitten by a mad dog and applied the roots of a wild rose to heal the wound. Wild roses assumed a special significance in the 15th century when there was a fierce struggle for the throne between the Houses of York and Lancaster. The warring factions adopted the white rose and the red rose respectively for their emblems. The conflict dragged on for thirty years and became known as the Wars of the Roses.

WAYSIDES IN BLOOM

In May and June waysides burst into flower and provide a marvellous show of different shapes and colours by day. At dusk some flowers, like the white campion, perfume the air to attract night-flying moths.

You cannot miss the lesser celandine in flower. Its brilliant shining yellow blooms nestle low in damp parts of hedgerows, woods, among meadow grasses and fall in golden cascades over rocks and stones by streams and ponds.

Each flower has between eight and twelve glossy petals, surrounded by three pale green sepals. After pollination by honey bees and other insects the flowers tend to lose their intense colour and towards the end of their life they become white and rather ragged. The leaves, fleshy dark green and hairless, are heart-shaped and borne on long stalks.

Goldilocks buttercup is another member of the buttercup family, but it is smaller and less hairy than the common meadow buttercup and is the only one to grow in woodlands and hedgerows. Its leaves are deeply divided and hairless. The flower may have five petals, but often one or more are missing; sometimes there are none at all. Then the sepals are a pale yellowish colour.

Cow parsley is one of the most common and delicate-looking members of the parsley family, and the first to bloom in spring. Its small white lacy flowers, a favourite of nectar-seeking insects like hoverflies, beetles, day-flying moths and butterflies, have five petals clustered at the tip of each stalk. The rigid, ribbed green stem is often tinged with purple and the fern-like leaves are separated into pairs of much-divided leaflets. Cow parsley is sometimes called wild chervil, and its young

Right: Male and female campion flowers appear on separate plants. This male red campion is fully developed and about to she pollen from its anthers.

Below: Flowers attract man different local names, but few are as appropriate and appealing as golden stars, the name given in Somerse to lesser celandines.

leaves add a mild spicy flavour to salads and stews.

The red and white campions, both members of the pink family, provide a glorious splash of colour to our hedgerows, particularly when they are mixed with bluebells and buttercups and surrounded by the lush green of young leaves and grasses.

The white campion's strong scent attracts night-flying moths such as the elephant hawk moth, but red campion, scentless, is pollinated by long-tongued bumble bees and hoverflies. The two species often interbreed and produce hybrids. Both have hairy green leaves that grow in pairs on the stem, becoming narrower as they reach the tip.

Herb robert can easily be identified as a member of the geranium family by the shape and strong smell of its hairy leaves. They grow in clusters at the end of long stalks and vary in colour from reddish brown, through a light to dark green. Small insects, such as some early hoverflies, pollinate the flowers. The plant's name is thought to have originated from a French monk, Abbé Robert, who founded the Cistercian order at the end of the 11th century. He used the leaves of the herb for healing a variety of ills.

The lesser periwinkle is a shrubby plant with blue-purple, mauve or white flowers that nestle separately in the axils of the leaves. As its name suggests, it is smaller than the greater periwinkle, though just as common.

Lesser periwinkle (*Vinca minor*) flowers March-May in woodland and hedgerows. Ht 50cm (20in).

Right: Herb robert (*Geranium robertianum*) flowers May-Sept in woods and hedgerows, on shingle and among rocks. Ht 50cm (20in).

Right: Goldilocks buttercup (*Ranunculus auricomus*) flowers April-May in hedgerows and woods. Ht 40cm (16in).

Below: Cow parsley (*Anthriscus sylvestris*) flowers April-June in hedgerows, waste places and beside woods. Ht 80cm (30in). Fruits are shown directly below.

Lesser celandine (*Ranunculus ficaria*) flowers March-May in damp hedgerows, meadows, beside streams. Ht 25cm (10in).

White campion (*Silene alba*) and red campion (*S. dioica*) bloom May-June—and white campion until Sept—in waste places. Ht 100cm (40in).

73

FIELD-SIDE AND HEDGEROW FLOWERS

Among the wide variety of wild flower species found in our field-sides and hedgerows are some that were once common in the fields as well. Some have become established at the field edge to escape the more rigorous modern farming methods, while others climb in profusion over summer hedgerows.

Above: **Hedge mustard** (*Sisymbrium officinale*), right, and **garlic mustard** (*Alliaria petiolata*), left.

The wild flowers growing at the edges of our fields today are fewer in number and variety than those found there 100 years ago. Many cornfield weeds, for instance, have disappeared from farm fields altogether as a result of modern farming methods. However, some species—finding the more protected and shadier conditions favourable—have remained, forming thriving colonies in the uncut grass and hedges at the field edge.

Hardy hedge-growers One such species, with many old local names aptly describing its location, is garlic mustard, also known as Jack-by-the-hedge and Jack-in-the-bush. In Elizabethan times the crushed leaves, which smell and taste of garlic, were used in a sauce eaten with boiled mutton or with salt fish; they are still used in spring salads today.

A shade-loving plant, it often grows in clumps in woodlands and against the dry stone walls of northern fields, as well as in sheltered hedgerows and shady corners of gardens and farmyards. The thin, pale green, triangular leaves are deeply and irregularly toothed and spread out below heads of small, white cross-shaped flowers which appear from April to June.

The hedge mustard, a related species, c[an] live through the winter, growing rapidly [in] the first mild days of spring to flower ear[ly] in the season. It is a stiff, wiry plant wi[th] twiggy branches growing at right-angles fro[m] the stem. The flowers appear from May [to] September and the stem elongates as t[he] flowers open, so that the small, new, p[ale] yellow flowers—shaped like a Maltese cros[s]—are always at the top of the stem. The uprig[ht] seed pods press tightly against the ste[m,] giving the plant an easily recognisable shap[e.] When ripe, the pods split from the botto[m] upwards, exhibiting a row of orange-brow[n] seeds along their length.

Invasive climber If a weed can be defined [as] a wild flower that is growing in the wron[g] place, then bindweed is one which can driv[e] gardeners and farmers to despair when [it] invades gardens and farm fields.

Once a weed of the cornfields, its attractiv[e] pink, or pink and white candy-stripe[d] flowers now appear by the wayside, o[n] derelict land and sometimes by the sea. [It] spreads rapidly by means of thick rhizome[s] that grow through the soil, rooting as deep a[s] 2m (6½ft) below the surface. The slende[r]

Left: The hedge bindweed (*Calystegia sepium*) grows in hedgerows and wood edges in the Midlands and southern England. It climbs by twining around the stems of other plants, always in an anti-clockwise direction. The trumpet-shaped flowers, reaching up to 7cm (2¾in), are the plant's most striking feature. In bloom from July to September, they first appear as long white buds with two broad red or green-streaked bracts at the base. These unfurl and remain wide open even at night, attracting the long-tongued convolvulus hawk moth, which arrives at dusk to feed from the nectar glistening at the base of the flower.

ralling overground stems, up to 75cm (in) long, twist around other plants – often tightly that they are choked and die.

A similar species is the hairy bindweed, ich has large, marshmallow pink flowers. is species was first brought from America to tain as a garden plant. It escaped and has come naturalised, now growing in more n 100 localities throughout Britain.

Mid-summer flowers The ox-eye daisy is a miliar flower of mid-summer fields and dsides. The single, conspicuous flower d, reaching up to 5cm (2in) across, is com- sed of many tiny, individual flowers or rets. Small, yellow tubular florets make up central yellow disc, surrounded by white, liating, strap-shaped ray florets. One des- ptive local name for this species is 'beams brightness'.

Mugwort, (*Artemisia vulgaris*) like the ox- e daisy, is another mid-summer flower. It s a rather dusty appearance and is often und growing by dry and dusty roadsides in e summer. The rather stiff branched stems ch heights of 120cm (4ft), but the wind- llinated flowers are very small, brown and her inconspicuous. The leaves are dark en above and lighter with grey-white hairs the underside.

Mugwort was believed to have magical operties. St John's Eve in June was cele- ated with bonfires, and mugwort plants re held in the smoke. They were then woven o garlands and hung over doorways to ep away evil spirits. The crushed leaves ve a slightly aromatic scent and they have en used as an infusion to make herbal teas.

Tough survivor Dandelions are one of our ost successful and conspicuous composites. nce their feathery fruits, each containing a gle seed, are widely dispersed on the wind, ndelions colonize recently cleared ground d, once established, their deep, long-lived d exceptionally tough roots help them to rvive all but the most determined efforts by an to remove them. Even a small piece of ot left in the ground can regenerate a whole ant within a very few weeks.

There are more than 100 types of dandelion d they grow in a great variety of habitats,

Above: The attractive flowers of the bindweed (*Convolvulus arvensis*) set few seeds, as the plant spreads successfully by its creeping rhizomes. Even if the plant is dug up, the tiniest remaining fragment can grow into a new plant.

including fields, waysides, chalk grasslands and wet marshes. They reproduce asexually. The seed embryos are not fertilised by insect pollination; confusingly, however, pollination is often required for the development of the seeds, and this happens when dandelions attract nectar-seeking insects.

Poisonous berries Black bryony (*Tamus communis*), a climber that needs the support of hedges, bushes and fences, is frequently found where a field is sited alongside a wood, or bounded by a fence or hedge. In the sum- mer the slender, flexible stems grow upwards, turning clockwise around the stems of other plants and reaching lengths of 3.6m (12ft). The glossy, dark green, pointed leaves spread out to catch and reflect the sun. The small spikes of yellow-green flowers are incon- spicuous and appear from May to July. Male and female flowers grow on different plants. Later, clusters of shining, but poisonous, red berries develop on the female plants.

In early autumn, the leaves turn a clear yellow, in striking contrast to the red berries. When the leaves have fallen, clusters of ber- ries are sometimes seen spaced along 'ropes' of stems twisted along a fence or through a hedge. The 'black' in the plant's name refers to the black fleshy roots which, like the berries, are poisonous. Cattle have been killed by eating the roots left heaped at the edge of their fields when the plants have been cleared from hedgerows.

Black bryony

Above: Ox-eye daisies (*Leucanthemum vulgare*) were once common in hay meadows. It is now more usual to find just a few plants in bloom from June to August at the field edge.

Below: **Field mouse-ear chickweed** (*Cerastium arvense*) flowers April-Aug in dry grassy areas especially on chalky soils. Ht 25cm (10in).

Right: **Meadow saxifrage** (*Saxifraga granulata*) flowers April-June in basic and neutral grassland in eastern areas. Ht 30cm (12in).

Right: **Purple saxifrage** (*Saxifraga oppositifolia*) flowers March-May, sometimes again in July, in damp, rocky areas. Ht 15cm (6in).

CHALK GRASSLAND FLOWERS

In chalky grassland areas you can find colourful and abundant plants such as vetches and trefoils which are easy to spot for their marvellously vivid blooms.

Vetches and trefoils are characteristic of chalky areas, and their bright yellow and purple flowers are distinctive in the grass, especially in ground that has been well grazed by animals such as sheep. Their pea-shaped blooms attract bees which visit them for pollen and nectar – you often see bumble bees busily working the blossoms, moving swiftly from one patch of flowers to the next. Vetches and trefoils can be either annuals or perennials. They all produce fruits in pea-shaped pods which, when ripe, crack open on dry, sunny days and disperse the seeds around the immediate area.

Bird's-foot trefoil, a colourful and plentiful perennial, is usually found growing in clumps on grassy slopes and also on young sand dunes. Groups of up to eight yellow flowers are borne at the end of the stalks which rise from the roots or creeping rhizomes and stolons. The flowers often have flecks of orange or red on the petals, particularly on the undersides before the buds have opened. The name, bird's-foot trefoil, refers to the leaflets, in groups of three, which look like a

bird's claw, arising from the stem. At base of the leaf stalk there are two le stipules.

Vetches Kidney vetch is a common a variable species of chalk grassland, parti larly in coastal areas. Its flowers are borne crowded heads, and may be yellow, oran red, and even purple or white. Kidney ve can also be annual or perennial and gro semi-prostrate or erect. It has two kinds green-silver leaves: oval ones arising from base and pinnate ones arising from higher the stem.

Another vetch, the horseshoe vetch, tra along the ground and bears numerous de yellow flowers. It derives its name from blooms which are arranged in a horsesh shaped cluster, and the pods that develop the form of interlocking horseshoes. T purple milk-vetch is a similar short dow vetch species but it is rare except in easte areas of the British Isles where you find it the coast. Its purple flowers are cluster together at the tip of the stem and they la develop into pods that are covered in wh hairs.

Mouse-ears Field mouse-ear chickwe and the rarer dwarf mouse-ear chickwee members of the pink family, both grow chalk grassland. The perennial field mou ear chickweed grows in dry areas, produci both rooting and flowering shoots from creeping stock. The plant is covered wi hairs, and the white flowers are borne sing The pairs of narrow leaves are reminiscent mouse ears in size and shape – hence t name.

The smaller dwarf mouse-ear chickwe flourishes in open chalk grassland or in qua ries in the southern half of England. You c easily recognise it by its sticky touch, t reddish-purple underside of the leaves ar

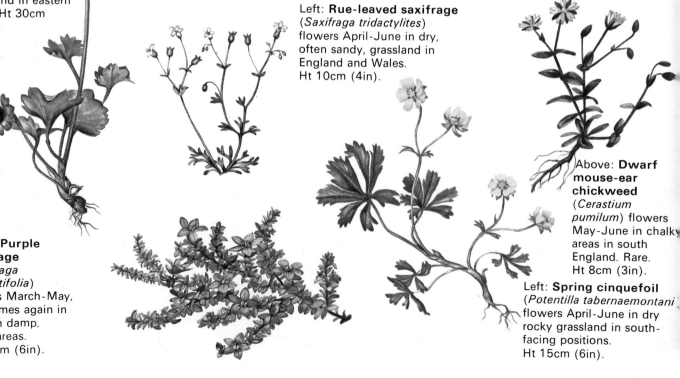

Left: **Rue-leaved saxifrage** (*Saxifraga tridactylites*) flowers April-June in dry, often sandy, grassland in England and Wales. Ht 10cm (4in).

Above: **Dwarf mouse-ear chickweed** (*Cerastium pumilum*) flowers May-June in chalk areas in south England. Rare. Ht 8cm (3in).

Left: **Spring cinquefoil** (*Potentilla tabernaemontani*) flowers April-June in dry rocky grassland in south-facing positions. Ht 15cm (6in).

Left: Purple milk-vetch is one of our less common flowers, but it is locally abundant in chalky soils.

Below: **Horseshoe vetch** (*Hippocrepis comosa*) flowers May-July in dry areas. Ht 20cm (8in).

seed pods

seeds

e transparent edges of the margins of the pper leaves.

Saxifrages There are 18 species of saxifrage owing in the British Isles, and all but one . *umbrosa*) are native – the exception has en introduced from the Pyrenees. Most of em are perennials, but the rue-leaved xifrage is an annual.

The downy meadow saxifrage is widespread dry and sandy grasslands where it grows ost commonly. Its white flowers are borne clusters at the end of the stem, and the few een leaves at the base of the plant are alked, kidney-shaped and toothed.

The rue-leaved saxifrage is a smaller ecies. It thrives in open chalky areas, as well on walls. It is an erect, sticky haired plant ith white flowers which appear in early mmer. The leaves are usually stalkless and ften have a reddish tinge to them.

The spring cinquefoil is a member of the se family which favours short chalk grass-nd and is one of 14 cinquefoils to be found the British Isles. It is a rare species that rows in mats, its hairy creeping stems

Above: **Kidney vetch** (*Anthyllis vulneraria*) flowers June-Sept in dry chalky places in shallow soils, often by the sea. Ht 40cm (16in).

Above: **Bird's-foot trefoil** (*Lotus corniculatus*) flowers May-Sept in grassland, by roadsides, in lawns. Ht 30cm (12in).

spreading over large areas, rooting themselves at intervals. The short-stalked, deep green leaves are usually divided into five and seven leaflets at the base of the stalk, but towards the tip of the plant there are only three, unstalked leaflets. Its bright yellow flowers form a beautiful carpet of colour in midsummer.

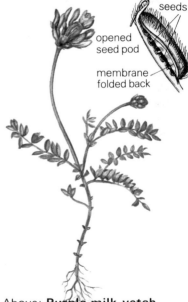

seeds

opened seed pod

membrane folded back

Above: **Purple milk-vetch** (*Astragalus danicus*) flowers May-July in short grass, on dunes and chalky soils. Ht 20cm (8in).

Left: Bird's-foot trefoil has over 70 local names, including 'old woman's toenails' in Devon and 'egg and bacon' in Somerset. It is one of the most abundant flowers of chalk and limestone areas.

Above: **Crown vetch** (*Coronilla varia*) is one of the many members of the pea family found on grassland. Introduced to the British Isles from the Mediterranean, it can grow to a height of 60cm (2ft), flowering June-August.

FLOWERS OF ROUGH GRASS AND TURF

Although the rolling downlands provide our richest grassland flora, wild flowers can be found in almost any grassy situation. Hedgerows, rough pasture, village greens, golf courses and the grassy borders of disused railway lines all provide a home for an interesting variety of species.

Grassland is a very diverse habitat. The variety of conditions under which it is formed, and subsequently managed, produces greatly differing selections of wild flowers. Generally, grassland on chalk or limestone is much richer in species than the acid grassland of our northern uplands. The length of the grass also has a direct influence on the type of the flowers to be found there.

Long grass If the grass is fairly long, there are likely to be fewer species present, because the smaller flowers are choked. In long grass, tall pioneer species such as the thistles grow best of all.

Thistles belong to the Compositae family, along with daisies, knapweeds and dandelions. On chalk or limestone soils, you may well come across the handsome musk thistle. It is the fragrant musk-like scent of its flowers that gives this species its name. The musk thistle is readily identified by its large pinkish-purple flower heads which, unlike other thistles, hang gracefully down under their considerable weight—hence the alternative name of drooping thistle.

Knapweeds, close relatives of the thistles, grow in hedgerows and in the long grass of rough pasture. They differ from thistles in that the edges of the leafy bracts surrounding each flower head are thin and papery, instead of drawn-out into sharp prickles. The greater knapweed has green bracts, while those of the lesser knapweed are blackish-brown. Both species are popularly known as 'hardheads'.

Clovers and vetch Where the grass is a little shorter, you will find the members of the pea family (Leguminosae). The peas, beans, lupins and laburnums of our gardens also belong to this family.

Red clover is a familiar grassland flower, and the rarer zig-zag clover, which is often confused with it, favours the same habitat. Zig-zag clover owes its name to the zig-zag growth of its stems, and it can be recognised by the noticeably flattened head of flowers, which is a much darker red than that of the red clover. More common in the north of Britain, it can be found if you look closely in dry pastures and bushy places.

Also closely related to each other are the

Thistle structure

The head of a thistle is not a single flower, but a capitulum—many tiny individual florets, packed tightly on to the flattened head or receptacle of the stem. Each floret is a long tube made up of five narrow petals, containing five male pollen-bearing stamens. The heads of the stamens fuse together to form a hollow column around the single female style. The stigma protrudes from the tube of petals (corolla), to catch the pollen carried by visiting insects. After pollination, a one-seeded fruit is formed at the base of the style, and when mature, a feathery outgrowth or pappus provides each tiny fruit with its own parachute.

ite or Dutch clover and the less common
ike clover. The latter, introduced as a
der crop, is more usually found as a weed
wing in cultivated land along roadsides.
iffers from the native white clover in that
never creeps along the ground; its tall
nched stems may reach a height of 60cm
t). From a distance, it can be recognised by
strong, pinkish tinge to the otherwise
ite flowers that actually grow more notice-
le as they fade.

A sunny, grassy bank is the preferred home
the wild liquorice, or milk vetch. Although
s is not the species from which commercial
uorice is obtained, a sweet juice was
merly extracted from its roots and used to
vour drinks. It is a stout, almost woody,
aggling perennial, and can be distinguished
sily from all the other vetches and peas
the oval heads of large, short-stalked,
enish-cream flowers and equally large
nate leaves. Mainly southern in distribu-
n and absent from Ireland, this local plant
vours limestone soils.

Small flowers of the turf Regular mowing on
lf courses, and close grazing by rabbits (on
used railway lines for example) results in a
ort, dense turf which usually produces a
de variety of small flowers, some of which
e characteristic downland species.

One of these, fairy flax, is well-named. It
s slender, thread-like stems, no more than
few inches high, and the plant would never
seen if it were not for the loosely branched
ads of small white flowers. Equally difficult
see, but often discovered unintentionally
picknickers who sit on it, is the dwarf or
emless thistle. Unlike other thistles, this
ecies rarely has a stem at all, its smooth
wer heads arising directly from a basal
sette of prickly leaves. It grows in dry, lime-
ch soils and has a deep tap-root which helps
e plant to survive long and severe periods of
 rought.

Eyebright is another typical plant of the
ort turf. Infusions of the plant were once
sed to treat eye infections – hence its name.
here are about 25 species of eyebright in
e British Isles, but the one you are most
kely to see is the widely distributed common
yebright. The plant is sometimes parasitic
n the roots of grasses, although it does pro-
uce its own food by the process of photo-
ynthesis.

Wasteland plants A hard, compacted sur-
ace, such as that found in many wasteland
reas, tends to create a thinly vegetated
rassland habitat which has its own charac-
eristic flora. Weld, also known as dyer's
ocket, is a plant found here. Similar in
ppearance to the wild mignonette (which is
weetly scented), it is a tall, stiff plant with a
ong narrow spike of greenish flowers. The
hole plant can be boiled to yield a beautiful
ellow dye, and before the introduction of
rtificial dyes, was much cultivated for this
urpose.

Above: **Wild mignonette**
(*Reseda lutea*) flowers
June-Sept on wasteland.
Unlike the garden variety,
the flowers are scentless.

Musk thistle (*Carduus
nutans*) flowers June-Aug, on
chalky soil, wasteland.
Ht 90cm (3ft).

**Lesser
knapweed**
(*Centaurea
nigra*) flowers
June-Sept on
grassland,
waysides. Ht
40cm (16in).

**Greater
knapweed**
(*Centaurea
scabiosa*) flowers
June-Aug. Ht 60cm
(2ft).

Stemless thistle
(*Cirsium acaule*)
flowers July-Aug.
Ht 20cm (8in).

DOWNLAND PLANT SURVIVORS

Downland flowers–like the hairy violet and the bulbous buttercup–have to be tough, for they must survive not only the attentions of grazing animals but also drought.

One of the main hazards for downland plants is grazing animals. But although tall-growing species are damaged beyond recovery by sheep and rabbits, low-growing, clump or rosette-forming species can survive, as can species that have a bitter taste or are poisonous–and are therefore left alone.

Downland plants must also be able to survive drought, since rainwater drains very quickly through the porous chalk and limestone. Some species manage to gain a roothold in the scrubland at the margins of downland, where grazing animals do not penetrate and where there is shelter afforded by tall grasses and hardy shrubs.

Small means survival There is a distinct ecological advantage to a plant in being small and low-growing on downland heavily grazed by sheep and rabbits. For instance, neither of the two most common grasses, sheep's fescue and red fescue, grow much above 50-70cm (20-28in) in height. Their two growth patterns, however, are different, the first being tufted while the second is creeping in habit. They are able to regenerate because grazing animals do not damage their lateral buds.

Many of the delicate downland species form a rosette of leaves pressed closely to the ground, down among the short grasses. One such species is chalk milkwort which grows locally, together with other species of milkwort, on chalk and limestone downland in the south of England. It is most abundant on the North Downs and in May its bright blue flowers carpet the slopes of Box Hill in Surrey.

On Box Hill chalk milkwort often mingles with the hairy violet, which is in flower at the same time. This is another typical early-flowering downland plant, but it grows in tufts rather than rosettes. Even so, it is small enough to avoid damage by grazing animals. There are probably two forms of the hairy violet growing on downland, one form flowering about two weeks earlier than the other.

Like all violets, the spring flowers of hairy violets are brightly coloured (blue-violet in this case), and they are cross-pollinated by

Above: You can find the bright mauve flowers of chalk milkwort only on chalk and limestone areas in southern England. Its leaves form a rosette close to the ground and it is small enough to avoid damage from grazing sheep and rabbits.

Right: Not all plants find the dry downland soils a disadvantage. Downland is famous for the number of orchid species growing there, many of them at the northern extreme of their range. The thin soil warms quickly in the spring and the summer 'baking' helps to ripen the seeds or the tuber of the orchids. The musk orchid (*Herminium monorchis*) shown here is a typical example; it grows on the chalk downland of south-eastern England and one of the smallest British orchids, reaching only 5-15cm (2-6in) in height. I grows only in full sunlight i the shortest of turf and reproduces vegetatively by underground tubers. Its yellow-green flowers are at their best at the end of June

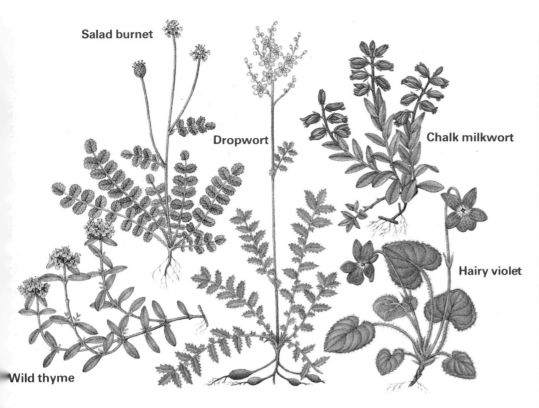

Salad burnet

Dropwort

Chalk milkwort

Hairy violet

Wild thyme

Chalk milkwort (*Polygala calcarea*). Flowers April-June on chalk and limestone downland in south-eastern England. Ht up to 15cm (6in).

Hairy violet (*Viola hirta*). Flowers May-Sept on chalk and limestone grassland. Hybridises freely with other violets. Ht up to 10cm (4in).

Salad burnet (*Sanguisorba minor*). Flowers May-Sept in dry grassy areas, mainly on limestone. Ht up to 30cm (12in).

Wild thyme (*Thymus serpyllum*). Flowers May-Aug on dry grassland and calcareous soils. Ht up to 7cm (2¾in).

Dropwort (*Filipendula vulgaris*). Flowers May-August on dry limestone grassland. Absent in Ireland and N. Scotland. Ht up to 70cm (28in).

sects. But hairy violets also produce cleistomous flowers later in the year. These are wers that never open and are self-fertilising. is probable that the rapid increase of violet pulations, which can take over an area of veral hundred square yards in two or three ars, is due almost entirely to the offspring oduced from the seeds of cleistogamous wers.

The hairy violet therefore does not need rely on the chancy method of insect llination in order to spread. However, we ow that the spring flowers also produce fspring, for hybrids between the various let species are common and can only have been produced by cross-pollination.

A plant with a nasty taste Most grazing animals (apart from the goat, which will eat practically any plant without ill effect) are not like lawn-mowers – they do not cut down all the plants indiscriminately. Some species are avoided, either because they are too tough to be palatable or because they are distasteful or even poisonous.

It is quite common to see the tall-growing bulbous buttercup which, like all buttercups, has an extremely unpleasant, acrid taste, growing well above the level of the grass on grazed downland pasture. The grazing animals leave a little tuft of other plants around the base of the buttercup, not wishing to get too close, thus providing small oases of cover for tiny flowers and insects that can flourish without being molested.

The bulbous buttercup is the first of the common buttercups to flower, blooming in May and June, and is the only one to have a swollen food store at the base of its stem. This is a corm, not a bulb, so the buttercup's name

Below: Rabbits find the leaves of the common rockrose (*Helianthemum nummularium*) unappetising and consequently leave them alone. This species grows in areas where the soil is thin and the chalk so close to the surface that the grasses are starved and grow very sparsely. In June the whole plant is a mass of yellow blooms, although the individual flowers last for only one day. The plant may well go on producing a few flowers all summer.

a strong, fresh flavour. They both begin
flower in May and their inflorescences
borne well above the leaf rosettes. The flow
of salad burnet are yellowish with purpl
red stigmas, while those of dropwort
creamy white and sweetly scented.

These plants are not usually found in
short turf of the heavily grazed areas, wh
their rosettes are too tall to avoid serio
damage. But they are characteristic of are
where grazing is light. Such areas are quic
invaded by grasses like the meadow oat a
the upright brome. The creeping and roset
forming downland species grow well in
light shade cast by these tall grasses.

However, if grazing ceases altogether, th
coarse grasses, tor grass for example, so
take over – to the extent that the downla
species die from lack of light and space. T
saplings from the chalk scrubland take ro
and characteristic shrubs like the wayfari
tree mingle with hawthorn and dogwood a
are festooned with the long trails of old ma
beard.

is a misnomer.

Surviving drought One of the most characteristic downland species is wild thyme.
Most of us associate this aromatic plant with
summer sunshine, but in fact it starts to
flower in May and continues throughout the
summer. There are many different subspecies
and varieties of this creeping mat-like species,
some with hairy and some with hairless leaves.
You can often find them growing with the
common rockrose, a species which flowers in
June and can be covered by a mass of yellow
blooms.

The wild thyme and the common rockrose
survive happily in this drought-prone situation, where water runs off the rocks and
drains from the thin soil very quickly. Both
species have creeping stems, which root where
they touch the surface of the soil (trefoils and
tormentils have a similar habit). The plants
cover a greater surface area in this way and
can therefore absorb water more quickly
when it rains. Their roots also penetrate deep
into the soil to tap the underground water,
which is much less likely to be exhausted in a
dry spell.

Plants of lightly-grazed land Sometimes,
at the very top of downland, rainwater drains
away so rapidly that all the calcium is leached
out of the soil with the water. This may lead
to the anomalous situation where the soil at
the top of calcium-rich downland may have
very little calcium.

Here lime-hating plants such as heathers
and gorse may grow. Often lime-loving
plants such as dropwort and salad burnet are
found growing with the lime-haters, for their
long tap roots penetrate so deeply that they
obtain their water from far beneath the surface where there is still plenty of calcium. A
strange mixed flora of this kind can be seen
at Lullington Nature Reserve on the South
Downs near Eastbourne.

Salad burnet and dropwort are both members of the rose family. They form rosettes of
pinnate leaves, those of salad burnet being
lighter green and smelling of cucumber, while
those of dropwort are darker green and resemble the leaves of a carrot. Salad burnet
leaves can be used in green salads; they impart

Above: The tall-growing
bulbous buttercup
(*Ranunculus bulbosus*) is
avoided by grazing animals
since, like all buttercups, it
has an unpleasant acrid
taste. The food store at its
base is a corm.

Many plants grow in the
more open areas of
downland and on the
margins of the scrubland.
One of them (shown belov
is crosswort (*Galium
cruciata*). This species, with
its whorls of leaves on wea
straggling stems and minut
straw-yellow flowers, is
unmistakably a member of
the bedstraw family. It is in
flower at the end of June.
While crosswort is typical
of the wetter marginal areas
meadow clary (*Salvia
pratensis*), pictured left, car
be found in drier areas,
although it is not very
common. It has bright
violet-blue flowers, which
appear in June, and
aromatic leaves. Like sage,
meadow clary is a herb; it
has many different folk-lore
names, including Provence
tea and Catalan sage.

TENACIOUS WEEDS OF THE FIELDS

The term 'weed' is applied to pioneer species, usually introduced, living in disturbed ground. However attractive a carpet of brightly coloured wild flowers in a field may be, their presence is not always welcomed by farmers.

Above: The dazzling bright yellow of the meadow buttercup can colour a whole field where the plants grow in abundance. These flowers are common in meadows and pastures.

In the intensively farmed lowlands of the British Isles there are a number of wild flowers that you will encounter on a walk along footpaths, across pastures or skirting arable fields; these are classed as 'weeds'. In pastures the farmer is only interested in grasses for his livestock; other plants may not be as nutritious and some are poisonous. In arable land only the crop, of course, is valuable. Weeds compete aggressively for space in the soil and can choke the crop plants, stunting their growth and so reducing yields at harvest time.

Meadow buttercup is one of the most characteristic plants of pastureland and sometimes grows in such abundance that the field acquires a hue of shimmering yellow. The flowers have a dazzling brightness; this is due to the glossy surface on the petals which strongly reflects sunlight.

Cattle and horses avoid eating meadow buttercups, which is just as well because they contain a powerful toxin that can prove fatal to livestock and cause severe stomach ache and sickness in humans. Only the fresh plants are dangerous, however. When they are cut and dried they lose their poisonous nature.

In some parts of the country they are also known as blister cups because juice from the stem and leaves can cause an itchy skin irritation.

Yellow rattle is another grassland weed, particularly common in old hay meadows. Its narrow, toothed leaves are arranged in pairs up the square stem which is topped with a loose spike of yellow flowers. The flowers emerge from a large light-green protective calyx in which the seeds are formed. Later, when the calyx becomes dry and husky, the ripe seeds rattle about inside – hence the name.

Yellow rattle is a semi-parasite. This means that although its leaves can manufacture food, and its roots can draw minerals from the soil, it also lives off the plants around it. Its roots attach themselves to the living roots of grasses and so tap into the grasses' own supply of soil nutrients. In fields where yellow rattle grows in profusion the grass growth is stunted and the resulting hay crop is reduced in bulk.

Sorrel Unlike many of its grassland neighbours, this native plant does not advertise its presence with a showy display of flowers. The inflorescence spikes are made up of numerous little green flowers tinged with red; there are no obvious petals. The rather inconspicuous flowers are dioecious – the male and female parts are borne on separate plants.

The leaves are arrow-shaped, the lower ones being stalked while higher up the plant they clasp directly on to the stem. The foliage is edible, with a pleasant sharp taste, and can be made into soup or used for flavouring sauces for meat dishes.

Corncockles were a familiar sight in our cornfields a hundred years ago; today they have virtually disappeared. Modern farming methods, particularly the spraying of chemical weed-killers (herbicides) on to growing crops have made them a rarity. The corncockle was regarded as one of the most troublesome weeds because its large seeds were not all removed when the wheat was 'cleaned' through sieves after the harvest. The seeds contain a mild poison which then became incorporated into bread, rendering it unwholesome.

The corncockle is a tall plant with hairy stem and narrow leaves. The solitary flowers, up to 5cm (2in) across, are a rich purple colour. Nectar is secreted at the base of the deep flower-tube and can only be reached by long-tongued pollinators such as butterflies.

Corn spurrey is still a common arable weed,

Left: **Sorrel** (*Rumex acetosa*) common in grassland, wood clearings in British Isles. Flowers May-Aug. Ht up to 100cm (40in).

Right: **Corncockle** (*Agrostemma githago*) rare, in arable land, especially cornfields. Flowers June-Aug. Ht 60cm (24in).

Above: The extensive use of herbicides has made the once-common corncockle quite a rarity in Britain's cornfields.

Below: **Venus's looking-glass** (*Legousia hybrida*) of arable land, chalk soils, esp S & E England. Flowers June-Aug. Ht 20cm (8in).

Right: **Common pepperwort** (*Lepidium campestre*) common in waste ground, fields; not in N Scotland, rare in Ireland. Flowers May-Aug. Ht 40cm (16in).

Left: **Chamomile** (*Chamaemelum nobile*) in dry grassy areas esp. sandy soils. Uncommon, not in Scotland. Flowers June-July. Ht 20cm (8in).

eferring dry, sandy soils. In some parts of rope it is grown as a fodder crop for estock. The narrow grass-like leaves are ranged in whorls, radiating at intervals m the stem. The tip of the stem divides into merous branches, each bearing a tiny wer with five glossy white petals. The wers are only fully opened on sunny days d quickly close should the sky cloud over.

Venus's-looking-glass is a plant with a nilar response to light and only opens its wers in warm sunny weather. These are ue-purple in colour, earning it the other me of corn violet. The plant is a weed of able fields, but is not very common nowa-ys.

Chamomile is a low-growing plant found cornfields, dry pastures and waste ground. has a creeping stock and spreads over the ound to form a compact mat. This habit is traditionally exploited in planted chamo-ile lawns and paths. The chamomile scented e air with a sweet smell, rather like apples, d the plant itself was credited with health-ving properties. In the mid-16th century illiam Turner wrote: 'It will restore a man his colour . . .'. Today its daisy-like wers are still used to make a refreshing rb tea. The species is remarkably resistant drought; during the dry summer of 1976 remained green long after all the surround-g grass had become parched.

Hedgerow crane's-bill, which probably ar-

rived from the Continent about 200 years ago, is still spreading through England. You should find it along lanes, hedge banks and field margins. It has hairy, reddish stems and the pink flowers are borne in pairs on side stalks. Pollination is carried out chiefly by bees and flies. When the long, beak-like seed capsule is ripe, it splits open violently. Each section springs backwards and hurls its seeds as far as three metres ($9\frac{1}{2}$ft) from the parent plant.

Dwarf spurge is a low-growing plant and like other spurges produces clusters of in-significant yellow-green flowers. The leaves are greyish-green and are joined directly on to the branched stems.

Right: **Hedgerow crane's-bill** (*Geranium pyrenaicum*) on road-sides, banks. Common in British Isles. Flowers May-July. Ht 25cm (10in).

Below: **Meadow buttercup** (*Ranunculus acris*) common in meadows, damp pastures in British Isles. Flowers May-Sept. Ht 60cm (24in).

Below: **Corn spurrey** (*Spergula arvensis*) common on arable land, esp. sandy soils in British Isles. Flowers May-Aug. Ht 25cm (10in).

bove: **Dwarf spurge** (*Euphorbia exigua*) common arable fields in British sles, rare in W Ireland & N cotland. Flowers May-Aug. Ht 20cm (8in).

Above: **Yellow rattle** (*Rhinanthus minor*) frequent in meadows, pastures in British Isles. Flowers May-July. Ht 25cm (10in).

85

GLORIOUS GRASSLAND ORCHIDS

Exquisitely constructed, most subtly coloured, and adapted to fascinating pollination procedures, orchids – rare or common – are a superb asset to the British flora.

Orchids, with their marvellous shapes and colours, have long fascinated man – as shown by their frequent appearance in folklore and popular medicine. One intriguing habit they have is to spring up suddenly in unexpected places – their seed is so light that it can be carried for many miles by the wind.

The roots of orchids are often fleshy or tuber-like. Many species have two underground tubers, one old, dark and shrivelled, the other newer, larger and lighter. The old one stores food being used to produce leaves and flowers while the younger one accumulates food for use the following season.

There are more than 25,000 species of orchid in the world, making the Orchidaceae one of the largest flowering plant families. Forty-nine species grow in the British Isles. Of these, many are also widely distributed in Europe, and areas as far away as Iran, Siberia and the Himalayas.

Some species, such as the common spotted orchid, thrive here in a variety of habitats, often in profusion. Others, such as the bog orchid, have a restricted distribution. Our most famous and spectacular species, the lady's slipper, is now all but extinct, apart from a secret site in Yorkshire where it is zealously guarded. The military and monkey orchids are also protected by law.

Most British orchids flourish on soils overlying chalk and limestone. Some particularly colourful and fascinating species can be found on the north and south downs of southern England, the limestone of north-

Pyramidal orchid
(*Anacamptis pyramidalis*) flowers June-Aug on chalk or limestone grassland and calcareous dunes. Ht 50cm (20in).

Bee orchid
(*Ophrys apifera*) flowers June-July in pastures, fields, copses, especially on chalk and limestone. Ht 45cm (18in).

Early spider orchid
(*Ophrys sphegodes*) flowers April-June in grassy areas on chalk or limestone in southern England. Ht 25cm (10in).

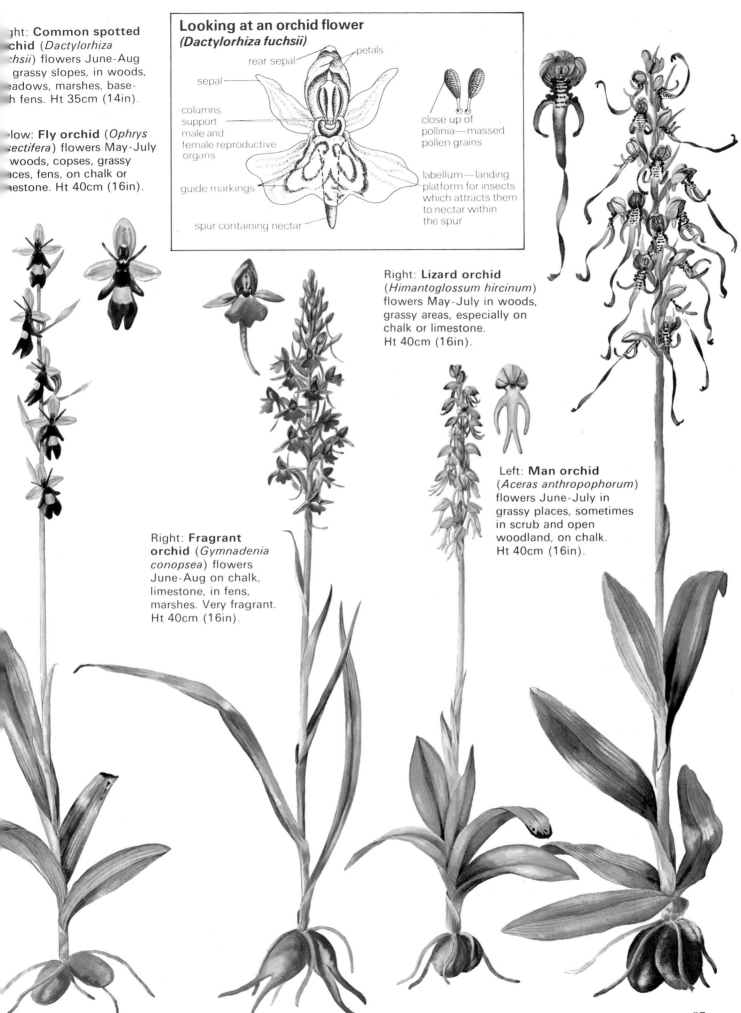

ght: **Common spotted** chid (*Dactylorhiza* hsii*) flowers June-Aug grassy slopes, in woods, eadows, marshes, base- h fens. Ht 35cm (14in).

low: **Fly orchid** (*Ophrys* sectifera*) flowers May-July woods, copses, grassy aces, fens, on chalk or estone. Ht 40cm (16in).

Looking at an orchid flower *(Dactylorhiza fuchsii)*

rear sepal

petals

sepal

columns support male and female reproductive organs

guide markings

spur containing nectar

close up of pollinia—massed pollen grains

labellum—landing platform for insects which attracts them to nectar within the spur

Right: **Lizard orchid** (*Himantoglossum hircinum*) flowers May-July in woods, grassy areas, especially on chalk or limestone. Ht 40cm (16in).

Right: **Fragrant orchid** (*Gymnadenia conopsea*) flowers June-Aug on chalk, limestone, in fens, marshes. Very fragrant. Ht 40cm (16in).

Left: **Man orchid** (*Aceras anthropophorum*) flowers June-July in grassy places, sometimes in scrub and open woodland, on chalk. Ht 40cm (16in).

87

Right: The man orchid, which has a labellum shaped like the trunk, arms and legs of a man, is one of our more common species that thrives on chalk or limestone soils.

Opposite page: The bee orchid, with its delightful colouring, is quite common on the chalk downs of southern England. It has numerous variations in colour and markings.

Below: The fly orchid. Pseudo-copulation is one of nature's most ingenious ways of ensuring cross-pollination: a male fly or wasp is attracted by the colour, shape and scent of the flower. Mistaking the flower for a female insect, the fly attempts to mate with it, and in doing so dislodges the pollinia (massed pollen grains) which become attached to its body and are then transferred to another flower of the same species.

ern England, and the Burren region of western Ireland.

Orchid flowering times are erratic: many species do not flower for several years after germination of their seeds. Once established, some, such as the fragrant orchid, may produce carpets of glorious pink-purple blooms in one year, but the same site may only have a few flowers the following season.

The seeds of most flowering plants germinate by using up their food reserves and then producing leaves so that photosynthesis can occur and growth can continue. Orchid seeds contain little nourishment. Instead it is provided by a fungus in the soil that surrounds the seed and helps the plant to

obtain food from dead organic matter. T communal relationship is known as a fung root (mycorrhiza) and it may continue several years—in some cases throughout orchid's life—and explains why some spe such as the pyramidal orchid can sp several years developing their root tub before producing leaves and flowers.

Orchids are monocotyledons, with seed leaf. The leaves are generally fleshy w straight parallel veins. All British orchids ground-dwellers, although tropical and c tivated species may be tree-dwellers or gr on stones.

Orchid flowers are rather more speciali than those of most other flowering plants. I comparison of the structure of a barr strawberry flower, for instance, with that the common spotted orchid, it can be seen th the strawberry has five regularly shaped sep and petals forming the outer portion of t flowers, and separate stamens and pistils. T common spotted orchid, however, li all the orchids, is quite different: has three outer sepals and three inn petals, forming the perianth. The low petal (labellum) is enlarged and is mc distinct in shape and colour. It is the lan ing stage for pollinating insects. The base the lip extends backwards into the sp which usually contains nectar.

On close examination you can see t sexual parts differ from those of oth flowers. The stamens and pistils are fused form the column, which lies above the ovar Only orchids have this column. The poll grains are massed together on two clu shaped structures (pollinia).

Other orchids, whether exotic tropic species, or the more modest British specie have a similar basic structure. The labellu is invariably one of the most distinguishir features and attracts pollinating insects. Th lizard orchid's labellum, for example, has long trailing ribbon-like central lip that coiled at first but gradually unfurls: it sometimes known as the tadpole orchid. Th fragrant orchid has a broad labellum on whic night-flying moths and butterflies land t probe down the deep slender spur for necta

Pollination In southern Europe man orchids and particularly *Ophrys* species a pollinated by bees and wasps in a proces known as pseudo-copulation—the male inse tries to mate with the flower, so pollinating i This is less common in the British Isles an the spectacular bee orchid is in fact sel pollinated: the tips of the pollinia, containin massed pollen grains, dangle over the stig mas and as the plant moves, the pollini brush the stigma and become attached to i The pyramidal orchid is pollinated exclus ively by long-tongued butterflies and haw moths. As they probe the long spur fo nectar, the pollinia are dislodged and stic to the proboscis, and are then transferred t other flowers.

PLANTS WITH DEADLY BERRIES

A wide-ranging family which includes cultivated species such as many familiar vegetables and ornamental garden species, the potato family also includes the poisonous, sometimes deadly, nightshades which grow in woodland, hedges and on waste ground.

The nightshades and related species belong to a large family of plants, the Solanaceae, which includes tomatoes, aubergines, peppers and tobacco. The best known member of the family is the humble potato which originates from central and southern America, but is now a staple crop in many countries, including Britain. The wild British members of the family are nearly as well known, but not for any edible qualities. Quite the opposite in fact, for most of them are extremely poisonous, especially the several different species bearing the name nightshade.

Scrambling climber Woody nightshade, or bittersweet, is a woody perennial common in damp places in hedges, woods and waste ground throughout Britain, although it is rarer in northern Scotland.

A quick-growing plant reaching up to 1.8m (6ft) high, woody nightshade is not truly a climber, but tends to scramble up and over other plants. A curious feature of the species is that the leaves are always aligned to face the sun, while the flower clusters always face away from the leaves. The purple petals spread out

Above: The flowers of woody nightshade resemble those of the potato but the petals are purple, rarely white like those of its cultivated relative. Clusters of the colourful berries (below) are often seen at different stages of ripeness.

when the flower first opens, and gradua curve downwards, completely away from t cone of bright yellow stamens in the centre the flower.

The oval berries are green at first, ripeni through orange to bright red and becomi almost translucent when fully ripe. They a produced in succession throughout the su mer and early autumn, and a plant may be fruit in all stages of ripeness while still flowe ing freely.

The plant has long associations with fol lore, and a necklace of its berries was four in the tomb of Tutankhamen. Closer home, the Vale of Furness in the north England was known locally as the Valley Nightshade because of the abundance woody nightshade that grew there; it w even depicted on the ancient seals of the loc abbey.

Garden dweller Black nightshade is a som what bushy annual reaching up to 60cm (2 in height. It is much less widespread than woody relative, being rather rare in northe England, Wales and Ireland and absent fro most of Scotland. Elsewhere, it is a successf weed and is widespread throughout much the rest of the world. Common on was ground, its frequent appearance in garde has earned it the alternative name of garde nightshade.

It is rather a lacklustre plant with dull gree foliage and small white flowers which a exactly like those of the potato. The flow clusters are unusual in that they arise fro the sections of stem between the leaves instea of from the more usual position in the le axil. The berries are round and, like those woody nightshade, are green when young b ripen to black.

A number of closely related species whic are very similar in appearance have bee introduced to Britain from various countrie For example, the South American speci *Solanum sarrachoides* closely resembles blac nightshade, apart from the berries whic remain green when fully ripe. The orange berried *Solanum pseudocapsicum*, the Jerusa lem cherry, often sold as a pot plant under th name winter cherry, is also occasional

...und growing wild in this country.

Satan's cherries Black nightshade is some-
...mes mistaken for the rarer and much more
...ngerous deadly nightshade or belladonna.
...oth plants have black berries, but there the
...semblance ends. Deadly nightshade occurs
...n chalk and limestone soils in England and
...ales, and is a rather bushy perennial, fav-
...uring shady spots in woods and thickets or
...ar old buildings where it may reach a height
...1.5-1.8m (5-6ft).

...It can be recognised by the lurid greenish-
...urple bell-shaped flowers which grow singly
...n the axils of the leaves, not in clusters like
...ose of black nightshade. The large, coarse
...aves grow in pairs, one member of the pair
...ways being much larger than the other. The
...und, very shiny berries surrounded by the
...een lobes of the calyx are sometimes called
...atan's cherries and are very attractive. This
...tractiveness is dangerous, since eating even
...ne or two berries can be fatal to children.
...irds, however, eat them without ill-effect,
...hough they are too large for most species to
...anage.

...The narcotic properties of the chemicals
...ontained in the plant made deadly night-
...hade valuable as a drug plant, and it was
...nce even cultivated in this country to supply
...he drug industry. Some of the old names,
...uch as sleeping nightshade, attest to its uses,
...nd it is still occasionally used in eye drops

Above: Black nightshade is common on waste ground, and its frequent appearance as a garden weed has earned it the name garden nightshade. The small white flowers are exactly like those of the potato plant.

Right: The spiny seed capsule of the thorn-apple splits into four segments when ripe, releasing numerous seeds. Most cases of poisoning are due to accidental eating of unripe seeds, which taste sweet.

Berries to beware of

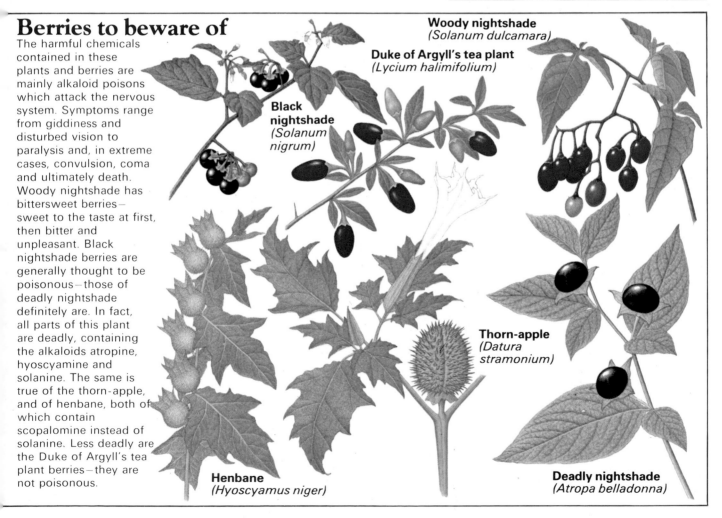

The harmful chemicals contained in these plants and berries are mainly alkaloid poisons which attack the nervous system. Symptoms range from giddiness and disturbed vision to paralysis and, in extreme cases, convulsion, coma and ultimately death. Woody nightshade has bittersweet berries – sweet to the taste at first, then bitter and unpleasant. Black nightshade berries are generally thought to be poisonous – those of deadly nightshade definitely are. In fact, all parts of this plant are deadly, containing the alkaloids atropine, hyoscyamine and solanine. The same is true of the thorn-apple, and of henbane, both of which contain scopalomine instead of solanine. Less deadly are the Duke of Argyll's tea plant berries – they are not poisonous.

Woody nightshade
(*Solanum dulcamara*)

Duke of Argyll's tea plant
(*Lycium halimifolium*)

Black nightshade
(*Solanum nigrum*)

Thorn-apple
(*Datura stramonium*)

Henbane
(*Hyoscyamus niger*)

Deadly nightshade
(*Atropa belladonna*)

spread to many countries. In Britain, it tu[...]
up fairly frequently as an alien, and sometir[...]
manages to establish itself in waste places a[...]
cultivated fields. Probably the most beauti[...]
member of the family, the thorn-apple [...]
large, solitary white flowers measuring up[...]
8cm (3in) long, the narrow tube flaring int[...]
trumpet-shaped bell. The flowers, which [...]
strongly scented, open at night and [...]
attractive to moths.

The thorn-apple takes its name from [...]
seed capsule which is similar in size a[...]
appearance to a horse-chestnut fruit. T[...]
whole plant is poisonous, not just the see[...]
although the effect of eating them is even m[...]
acute than in the case of deadly nightsha[...]
For this reason, farmers uproot and burn [...]
plant whenever it appears among their cro[...]

Harmless nightshades Not all members [...]
the nightshade family are harmful. The tub[...]
of the potato, for example, are our m[...]
common vegetable although the tomato-l[...]
berries are poisonous. The well known orr[...]
mental species, the Chinese lantern or ca[...]
gooseberry which occasionally escapes fr[...]
gardens and establishes itself in hedgero[...]
produces no ill-effects. The single flow[...]
resemble those of black nightshade but t[...]
calyx gradually enlarges, becoming pape[...]
and bladder-like, eventually turning brig[...]
orange to form the lantern of the plant's nan[...]
Within this lantern is a fleshy red berry.

The Duke of Argyll's tea plant, anoth[...]
harmless species, was popular as a gard[...]
plant with the Victorians, but has since fall[...]
out of favour. However, it has made a hor[...]
for itself on waste ground, old walls a[...]
waysides. A rather elegant shrub with archir[...]
pearly grey stems armed with spines, it h[...]
funnel-shaped purple flowers, followed [...]
egg-shaped, scarlet berries.

Above: Henbane is found on sandy soils, especially near the sea or on waste ground. It can be recognised by its thick growth, the flowers which have prominent purple or violet coloured veins, and the often strong and unpleasant odour of the whole plant.

Left: The intriguing name of the Duke of Argyll's tea plant arose when a specimen, wrongly labelled as a tea plant, was sent to the Duke of Argyll in the 18th century.

Below: The brilliant orange lanterns of the Chinese lantern (*Physalis alkekengi*) are not flowers. They appear in the late summer and contain a fleshy red berry.

for dilating the pupil of the eye. Italian ladies used it in this way in previous centuries to make their eyes more attractive, and this is said to be the origin of the Latin name *bella-donna*, meaning beautiful lady.

Stupefying herb Henbane is easily recognised by its flowers which are a whitish yellow with prominent purple or violet-coloured veins. They grow in two rows on long, coiled, one-sided spikes. Unlike most other members of the family, henbane does not produce berries. Instead, the fruit is a capsule completely hidden within the tubular calyx. The top of the capsule acts as a lid, falling away to allow the seeds to escape.

The whole plant has an unpleasant odour which, in large concentrations, is said to cause giddiness and stupor. Although the leafy tops are used to produce a sedative drug, henbane is very poisonous and should be left strictly alone.

Dangerous alien The thorn-apple is variously thought to have originated in North America, South America or somewhere in the Old World. Wherever its home was, it has now

RICH PICKINGS

The countryside in late summer offers a tasty array of edible fruits. Blackberries are very common, but there are a number of allied species that are just as succulent and worth the hard search.

Summer and autumn are the seasons when both humans and a great number of animals in the countryside can take advantage of the bounty of wild fruits offered by our hedgerows and fields. Most wild fruits are produced in far greater abundance than is ever needed merely to perpetuate the species, and they provide a vitally important source of food — for mammals such as foxes which do not always find animal prey in winter; for insects such as queen wasps which need to provision themselves for survival through the long winter months; and for huge numbers of migrant birds (fieldfares and redwings, for example) which come to Britain from northern Europe in search of just such resources.

The blackberry and its relatives The blackberry or bramble (*Rubus fruticosus*) is the most familiar member of the genus *Rubus*, which is represented in the British Isles by five main species (the raspberry, stone bramble, cloudberry, dewberry and the bramble itself). At the same time it is the most puzzling of our shrub groups, being so variable that, at the last count, more than 2000 variants, variously called sub-species, varieties, forms and cultivars, had been described. More are added every year.

Brambles vary considerably in the form, shape and colour of their leaves and flowers and in the flavour of the fruit. What is unchanging, however, is the fact that the blackberry is perhaps the fruit most favoured by an incredibly wide variety of mammals, insects and birds. It is, too, the fruit most familiar to us — as testified by its widespread use in jams, jellies and pies. Even today, when so much land is being reclaimed for farming or urban use, the blackberry can be found from August to October in almost any area of waste land, scrub, thicket, hedgerow or woodland.

All our native *Rubus* species produce edible fruits. The wild raspberry is the origin of all garden varieties and has been in continual cultivation for many centuries. The fruit is soft, red and juicy and, unlike the blackberry, is easily pulled away from its cone shaped receptacle.

The dewberry, which always has pure white

Blackberries provide delicious fruits from August to early October. They are a rich reward on late summer walks, and when gathered in quantity they make superb jellies, jam, pies and even wine. They are one of the few species you can pick without feeling guilty; bushes growing in the open produce hundreds of berries every season.

blossom, bears a fruit consisting of a few large, black, succulent drupelets that are covered with a dusty, greyish bloom. The stone bramble produces a crimson berry which has an excellent flavour. Cloudberries, which are a rich orange red colour when ripe, are much larger than blackberries. They have a pleasantly sharp taste.

The seeds of all these *Rubus* species rely on birds for their dispersal. The juicy, brightly coloured fruits act as a bribe to birds for the favour of carrying away the pips and depositing them elsewhere. Many mammals too – apart from man – are fond of the berries, although they disperse the seeds over a more limited area than birds.

Fruits of upland areas Two members of the *Vaccinium* genus have long been popular as culinary fruits. These are the cranberry and the bilberry.

Both flourish on acidic soil and are typically found in boggy moorland ground, acid woodlands and on heaths, often in fairly inaccessible places.

The cranberry, which flowers from June to August, has slender creeping stems about 30cm (12in) long that lie along the ground,

while the bilberry, in bloom from July to September, is a more shrubby plant, growing to a height of about 60cm (2ft). Both fruit in late summer and early autumn, the bilberry sometimes in such profusion that it forms 'bilberry moors' in which it is the dominant plant species. The fruits of the cranberry are red or brownish in colour; the bilberry fruit is black with a blue-grey bloom on the skin.

The fine flavour of the bilberry is excellent

Above: The pure white berries of the snowberry, which appear in the month October, are edible.

Right: The hedge brown butterfly is invariably associated with brambles. The adults feed exclusively on bramble blossom.

Edible berries

Below: **Blackberry** (*Rubus fruticosus*) or **Bramble** is widespread on heaths, in woods, waste places, scrubland. Flowers June onwards, fruits Aug-Oct. Makes good jelly, jam, puddings. Eat raw or cooked.

Right: **Dewberry** (*Rubus caesius*) grows on dry grassland and scrub, and in the Fens. Less common in Scotland. Flowers June-Sept, fruits late summer. Eat like a blackberry.

Right: **Stone bramble** (*Rubus saxatilis*) found in rocky upland areas. Flowers July, fruits early autumn.

Left: **Raspberry** (*Rubus idaeus*) grows on heaths, in woodland. Flowers June onwards, fruits Sept. Eat raw or cooked.

Above: **Cloudberry** (*Rubus chamaemorus*) found on moors, bogs. Fruits early autumn. Eat cooked.

when the fruit is eaten raw, but it is also good in jams and pies and as a flavouring for foods like ice cream. It is rich in vitamins C and D and has been used to make a purple dye. The cranberry is most famous as cranberry sauce—the traditional accompaniment to turkey—but is also good for jam and tarts.

A third member of the *Vaccinium* genus, the cowberry, can also be found on moors and heaths. Its red berries, which appear in September, are rather acidic in taste and therefore not as popular as those of its relatives.

Other fruits Another wild fruit that is sometimes eaten by man is the wild strawberry; this fruit, which appears in summer, has a fairly sweet taste but it is unfortunate that the fruits are generally too small and hard to be useful in cooking. They can be found in woods, scrub and grassland throughout Britain, especially on chalky soils.

Several other fruits found in the countryside are edible, but their flavour is not sufficiently good to recommend their use in the kitchen. They include the snowberry, originally a planted species but now found wild in hedges.

Left: **Snowberry** (*Symphoricarpos rivularis*) planted, also wild in hedges. Fruits Oct. Edible.

Above: **Bilberry** (*Vaccinium myrtillus*) grows on moors and heaths. Fruits Sept onwards. Eat raw or cooked.

Below: **Cranberry** (*Vaccinium oxycoccos*) grows in northern bogs, marshes. Fruits late summer. Edible.

Below: **Barberry** (*Berberis vulgaris*) is now rare in hedgerows. Fruits Oct., but hard to find. Good to add as flavouring.

Above: **Cowberry** (*Vaccinium vitis-idaea*) grows on moors in the north of the British Isles. Fruits Sept. Good for jelly.

Insects of field and hedgerow

Many of the constituent plants of the patchwork landscape–a motley habitat–are outstandingly rich in pollen, nectar and fruit. As such, scrub and hedgerow are vital fuelling stations for legions of invertebrates, among which the prime consumers are flying insects–flies, butterflies, bees and their allies, and wasps. At dusk, the night-flying insects, principally moths, replace this more varied dayshift. Scrub also provides the shelter that ensures insects have an excellent return for their foraging effort; a hedge of hawthorn, embroidered with clematis, bryony, honeysuckle or ivy, forms an effective break against energy-sapping wind.

An exceptional provider is the hawthorn, which has been shown to support over 50 species of insects, most of them drawn to its flowers. On the wayfaring tree, in contrast, the community concentrates more on the leaves; here, the abundance of leaf tissue and sap allows aphids to excel, even though they are checked by a string of predators–lacewings, hoverflies, bugs, beetles and spiders. Adjacent to such patches, open fields, meadows and downland are dominated by wild flowers and grasses. Butterflies achieve their greatest diversity here, each choosing some particular species of plant for egg-laying and caterpillar development. Grasses are the staple diet of the various 'browns' and also some of the 'skippers', but the butterfly community reaches its highest expression in chalk downland, the home of the dazzling 'blues'.

Collectively this insect fauna is an ancient one that has had the time to evolve elaborate life histories and sign language of great eloquence. Night-flying moths lay delicate scent trails in the wind to attract mates, while butterflies, with the advantage of daylight, flash iridescent colours to allure. Grasshoppers and crickets have come to depend on vocal signals, each species adopting a unique song to woo partners and shout down rivals. This need for unambiguous communication was never more necessary than in the hectic social life of ants and bees; in a given colony the ability of members to recognise the unique body odours of their own kin guarantees harmony within the nest and rapid detection and expulsion of infiltrators.

CHECKLIST

This checklist is a guide to the insects and other invertebrates you will find in fields and hedgerows. Although you will not see them all in the same place, you should be able to spot many of them as you walk through the countryside during the changing seasons. The species listed in **bold** *type are described in detail.*

Banded snail
Blood beetle
Brimstone butterfly
Buff-tailed bumble bee
Centipede
Click beetle
Comma butterfly
Common blue butterfly
Common bush cricket
Common swift moth
Common wasp
Cranefly
Dor beetle
Earthworm
Earwig
Garden spider
Gatekeeper butterfly
Greenbottle fly
Green lacewing
Green grasshopper

Harvestman
Holly blue butterfly
Holly leaf miner fly
Hoverfly
Large hawthorn sawfly
Large skipper butterfly
Large yellow underwing moth
Leafhopper
Marbled white butterfly
Meadow brown butterfly
Money spider
Nettle aphid
Orange-tip butterfly
Red ant
Seven-spot ladybird
Small skipper butterfly
Speckled wood butterfly
Spittlebug
Woodlouse
Yellow meadow ant

Above: Burnet moths – bright, day-flying grassland insects.

Left: The painted lady butterfly is a migrant, visiting Britain from the Continent in spring and early summer.

SUMMER HEDGEROW BUTTERFLIES

The hedgerow contains a trio of early summer butterflies – the orange-tip, holly blue and dingy skipper – with all the foodplants, nectar and sunny spots for basking they need.

The brightly-coloured orange-tip and holly blue butterflies are a familiar sight along lanes and hedgerows in most parts of Britain in early summer. The adult holly blue appears in early April while the orange-tip adult is on the wing from late April or the start of May; but they have very different life-styles. A third early summer butterfly, the dingy skipper, cannot match the other two for beauty – it fully lives up to its unprepossessing name – but its life-cycle is particularly fascinating.

Coloured for camouflage Only male orange-tips actually have the conspicuous, orange-tipped wings; the females have white wings with small black and grey markings. However, when any orange-tip – male or female – settles with wings closed, you'll be lucky to see it at all. The undersides of the hind wings look like a mottled patchwork of white and green markings. When the butterfly settles among the white flowers and green stalks of hedge parsley (one of its foodplants), it is very well hidden. If you look closely at the green markings you'll see that they are really a mixture of black and yellow scales. This trick – the same used by impressionist painters – makes the orange-tip one of the best camouflaged of all British butterflies; it is necessary because the orange-tip, like most butterflies, is unable to produce green pigments on its wings.

Female orange-tips seek out hedge parsley, cuckooflower and garlic mustard plants which are in flower in May and June when the adults are about. Each female lays only one egg to a plant; she positions the egg on the stalk of a flower that will have turned into a young seed pod by the time the caterpillar hatches just one week later. The caterpillar grows to full size in less than four weeks, feeding on a rich diet of seed pods and seeds rather than leaves. If there were two caterpillars on one plant they would probably run out of seed pods – which is why the female is careful to lay her eggs singly. Orange-tip caterpillars are also cannibals: if another female lays an egg on a plant already occupied, the older caterpillar will eat the younger one.

Early in July the caterpillar leaves its food-plant, which will die down in autumn, and

finds a dry stem on which to spend the winter as a chrysalis. It supports itself from the stem by a girdle that passes round its middle. The camouflaged chrysalis stage lasts for nine to ten months, until the following spring. The entire active life of the butterfly and its caterpillar stage is squeezed into the spring and early summer because only then are the foodplants at the right stage of growth.

The holly and the ivy Like the orange-tip, the holly blue overwinters in chrysalis form. Unlike the orange-tip, however, its food-plants have evergreen leaves so the chrysalis can safely attach itself to the underside of a leaf. The adult butterfly emerges from the chrysalis in April and flits around tall holly bushes but very rarely visits any flowers to drink nectar. When it does need moisture, it usually takes water from the damp soil at the edge of a puddle, or even from the foul smelling liquid on top of a cow pat. You can often see them sitting on paths or rides near a patch of moisture.

In May the female butterfly – distinguished from the male by the broad black borders on her wings – lays her eggs among holly flowers, spacing them out carefully. The caterpillar hatches quickly, eats any smaller caterpillars it finds, and feeds up rapidly on the nutritious flower buds and young fruits (rather than the tough leaves) of the holly. The caterpillar pupates in July. In some years this chrysalis stage lasts right through winter, but more

Above: Male orange-tip (*Anthocharis cardamines*) on cuckooflower. Look for it in hedgerows in May and June

Identifying orange-tips

Caterpillar – it is fully grown in about 26 days.

Female – could be mistaken for a cabbage white butterfly

Male – the only one with orange tips on the wings.

Left: Male and female holly blues (*Celastrina argiolus*) mating. This is the only blue butterfly to favour trees.

Identifying holly blues

Caterpillar—inactive, and occurs in 3 colour forms.

Male—distinguished by the sky-blue upper wing surface.

Female—has a noticeable black border on forewings.

ten the chrysalids hatch as a second, summer generation of adult butterflies. This second generation lays eggs on ivy flowers—holly is not available since it is only in flower early in the year. The holly blue is unique among British butterflies in that it alternates between foodplants in this way. The second generation caterpillar feeds up until late August, then pupates and spends the winter months in the form of a chrysalis.

Holly blues are most common in the south of England, and are absent from Scotland. In some years they are very common—probably after a couple of years in which good weather enables both spring and summer generations to breed successfully—and then they may become rare for a few years. It is a species that is often found in towns.

The Dingy Skipper

The dingy skipper, in common with others of its family, is more closely related to moths than to other butterflies. It usually rests just like a moth—with wings folded down across the abdomen. The chrysalids are even more moth-like, being protected inside a silk cocoon instead of exposed to view on a twig or stalk. The adults are on the wing in May and June, and fly in typical skipper fashion—a darting, frenzied flight. You'll find them in localised colonies in hedgerows, rough meadows and downland, particularly in chalky areas. The dingy wing colour is good camouflage, so you may have to search carefully.

In May the females lay their eggs singly on bird's foot trefoil—the only food plant of the caterpillar. The eggs hatch in a couple of weeks and the caterpillar stitches leaves together with silk to make a shelter, living inside well hidden from predators. It eats the leaves and therefore has to rebuild the shelter regularly. Instead of turning into a chrysalis, the dingy skipper caterpillar spins a cocoon and stays inside it—as a caterpillar—from July or August until very early spring. Only then does it turn into a chrysalis, hatching as an adult butterfly in a few weeks. In some areas, particularly in the south-west, there may be a partial second brood—in favourable years appearing in August and September if the early larvae pupate instead of becoming dormant.

The dingy skipper (*Erynnis tages*) lays its eggs singly on bird's foot trefoil.

egg (life-size)

Egg actual size, on leaf. The larva stitches 3 leaflets together with silk to make a hiding place.

egg (greatly magnified)

Below: When egg is first laid it is lemon yellow deepening eventually to apricot-orange.

larva

Larva, fully grown after 65 days, sews itself up in leaflets and spins a cocoon—a hibernaculum—in which it stays till the following spring.

pupa

The pupal stage occurs inside the hibernaculum and lasts 30-36 days after which the adult emerges.

SKIPPER BUTTERFLIES

Skipper butterflies, with their moth-like muscular bodies, differ in appearance from other butterflies. Their distinctive, rapid, darting flight gave them their name.

Skippers belong to the Hesperiidae family and in their wing and body structure are very distinct from 'true' butterflies. Like most butterflies they fly by day and have antennae thickened or clubbed at the tip, but they can be distinguished by their quick, darting flight and thick muscular bodies.

The head is wide with the antennae bases well separated, and the antennal club usually ends in a sharp point. The caterpillar, which is usually green or brown, lives in a cell of silk and folded leaves, tapering slightly at each end. Like many moth caterpillars, it pupates in a silken web or cocoon. The pupae of almost all other butterflies are naked, silk being used only to suspend them.

Distribution Eight species of skipper are found in the British Isles. Five are fairly common, though even these tend to have a southerly distribution. The other three are very localised and rare. None of the species produces more than one generation a year, but the life-history of each varies.

The distribution pattern of the skippers is interesting. Only the dingy skipper has ever progressed as far as Ireland, but it is most common in the south of England and Wales. Six of the others have ranges that extend from southern England northward in varying degrees. The large skipper reaches southern Scotland, while the small and grizzled species are found all along the south coast to the

Above: Although not apparent in this pair of mating large skippers, the male is easily distinguished from the female by the dark coloured 'sex-brand' on its forewing, which it uses during the courting ritual.

Below: The grizzled skipper (*Pyrgus malvae*) is quite similar in character to the dingy skipper. At night both adopt the folded-wing resting position more commonly associated with moths.

rthern Midlands. The Essex is predom-
antly a south-eastern species, thinning out
rapidly to the west and north; and the silver-
spotted species is confined to the chalk of
southern England.

The Lulworth skipper is the most localised
of all British butterflies, restricted as it is to a
small area on the south coast. The distribution
of the chequered skipper is something of a
puzzle. It was probably once widespread in
Britain, but encountered climatic conditions
which drastically reduced its population in all
but two widely separated regions. Unhappily,
it is now extinct in one of these, probably due
to the destruction of its habitat.

Dingy skipper As its name suggests, this
is a rather drab little butterfly, but it is one
of the commonest species. In all but one of
its habitats it appears in its 'ordinary' form,
but in the Burren of Clare in Ireland, a limestone district, the dingy skipper has rather
different characteristics. It develops handsome markings of dark brown and pale grey,
which are far from 'dingy' in any descriptive
sense. These butterflies are recognised as a
distinct sub-species under the name *baynesi*.

In England the dingy skipper is common in
the south, becoming less so further north,
and is known in Scotland in only a few
localities. It flies during the sunny days of
May and June, in dull weather resting on dry
seed-heads or grass and looking more like a
moth than a butterfly.

The males of this and the grizzled species
have special scales – called androconia – in a
fold on the front edge of their forewings.
These scales are scented and are scattered
during courtship and mating to stimulate and
arouse the female. The caterpillar is fully
grown in August and feeds on bird's-foot
trefoil. It spins a cocoon in which it hibernates,
pupating the following April.

Grizzled skipper This is the smallest of the
family and is easily recognised by its even
black and white checks. It flies in May and
June and is commonly found on chalk downs
and in open woodland as far north as
Lincolnshire. The caterpillar feeds on various
small plants, such as wild strawberry and
cinquefoil, and it overwinters as a pupa.

Large skipper This butterfly is found all
over England and Wales and in Scotland to
just north of the Solway Firth. As with the
small and Essex species, the sexes of the large
skipper butterflies are easily distinguished by
an oblique black streak of androconial scales
on the forewing of the male – often referred
to as the 'sex-brand'. These scales serve the
same function in mating as those on the
dingy skipper, although in that species they
are carried on a different part of the wing.

The large skipper flies from June to early
July and is common in all kinds of grassy
places, both in woods and in open country. In
common with the caterpillars of the small
and Essex skippers, as well as those of the
three rare species, the caterpillar of the large

Above: The dingy skipper is
the only one that occurs in
Ireland. This is probably
due to the fact that this
island was cut off from the
mainland by the sea long
before south-east England
was separated from the
European Continent. After
the retreat of the glacial
ice-sheets, animals spread
from the south into the land
that is now Britain. The
hardiest of these (the dingy
skipper included) came
earliest and were able to
cross into Ireland.

Left: A small skipper rests
on a muskthistle, a flower
to which, along with
burdock and knapweed, it is
particularly attracted. The
caterpillar, however,
develops on soft grasses
(like timothy and cat's tail)
which it uses as its
foodplant. It draws grass
blades together and spins
a silken cocoon to form a
pupal shelter.

Large skipper
(Ochlodes venata)

Dingy skipper
(Erynnis tages)

Small skipper
(Thymelicus sylvestris)

Above: The Essex skipper (*Thymelicus lineola*), was not recognised as British until 1890. It closely resembles the small skipper, but their life histories differ greatly. The Essex skipper's eggs do not hatch in winter, although the caterpillar inside is fully formed. It emerges in spring and feeds throughout May, before pupating in June. The butterfly can be seen in July, a few weeks after the first small skippers appear.

skipper feeds on grasses, seeming to prefer cock's foot and slender false brome grass. It hibernates as a half-grown caterpillar.

Small skipper Very common in southern and central England, this butterfly can be found as far north as North Yorkshire in the east but only to northern Wales in the west. Generally it is tawny yellow, but straw-coloured to almost white specimens are seen occasionally. In 1978 a remarkable blue small skipper was seen and photographed near Selborne in Hampshire. The clubs of the antennae are black above and orange-yellow below—an important feature in distinguishing this species from the Essex skipper.

The small skipper flies from the end of June to early August. It prefers damp plac[es] although it can be found wherever long gra[ss] is growing within its range. The caterpill[ar] hatches in August, makes a meal of its o[wn] egg-shell and then spins a cocoon in which [it] passes the next eight months of its life witho[ut] moving. The following April it emerges a[nd] feeds on Yorkshire fog and other soft-leav[ed] grasses until it pupates in June.

Essex skipper This is one of the most rece[nt] resident species of butterfly to be added to t[he] British list—the delay in detection being due [to] its very close resemblance to the small skipp[er.] It was not realised that both species existed [in] Britain until 1890 when specimens fro[m] Essex were recognised. The most obvio[us] feature separating the two is the colour [of] the antennal clubs—black in the Essex a[nd] orange underneath in the small skipper.

However, this butterfly is by no means co[n]fined to Essex. It is most common in sout[h] east England but has been recorded in a fe[w] localities in the south-west—Lincolnshi[re] marks its northern limit. It seems to pref[er] grassy places near the coast, although it [is] found inland as well.

Its life-history is different from that [of] the small skipper; the eggs are laid on gra[ss] stems and the caterpillar overwinters with[in] the egg. It emerges to feed in April, pupat[es] in June and is usually on the wing in Ju[ly.] Although it appears later than the sma[ll] skipper, the two are often seen flying togeth[er.]

Three rare skippers

Silver-spotted skipper Resembling the large skipper on its upper side, but with a dark green underside spotted with silvery white, this species is now restricted to a few localities in the Chiltern Hills and North Downs. Its decline is due partly to extensive cultivation of the downs, and to the decrease in grazing by sheep and rabbits, which has led to the grassy meadows becoming overgrown with bush scrub. It flies in August.

Lulworth skipper Even rarer, this species is confined to one area on the Dorset and Devonshire coast. The male resembles that of the small and Essex skippers but is darker and duller in colour. The female is marked with unmistakable pale yellowish spots on the forewing. It flies above the sea cliffs in July and August.

Chequered skipper The rarest British skipper (shown right) and very distinctive—both sexes are blackish spotted with yellow. Believed to be extinct in 1942, it was discovered unexpectedly in western Inverness-shire—now its only British habitat. It is on the wing from May until the end of June.

Silver-spotted skipper
(*Hesperia comma*)

wings closed

Lulworth skipper
(*Thymelicus acteon*)

Chequered skipper
(*Carterocephalus palaemon*)

FIVE BROWN BUTTERFLIES

Our sombre brown butterflies are characterised by the eye spots on their wing margins and by the fact that they walk on only four legs, the other pair having been reduced to useless brush-like appendages.

Out of the more than 120 different European species of butterflies belonging to the Satyridae family, only 11 are indigenous to the British Isles. Here we describe five typical, widely distributed British species: the speckled wood, marbled white, gatekeeper, meadow brown and ringlet.

The Satyridae are known as the 'browns' because various shades of brown are the predominant hues in the majority of species. The beautiful black and white chequered pattern of the marbled white is an exception.

The browns are medium-sized butterflies, their chief characteristics, apart from their prevailing colour, are the possession of eye spots on the wing margins, swollen veins at the bases of their forewings, bands of often conspicuous scent scales (androconia) in the males, and a degenerate first pair of legs. Because their foremost pair of legs are reduced to brush-like appendages, the browns walk only on the four remaining legs, like their cousins the Nymphalid butterflies (fritillaries and tortoiseshells).

Distraction display Almost all browns have black and white eye spots on the wing margins; those at the tips of the forewings are often especially large and conspicuous. In some species the eye spots are arranged in rows, while in others they are much reduced or even virtually absent. In the marbled white they are confined to the underside of the wings.

Above: A pair of marbled white butterflies (*Melanargia galathea*) mating. When a male Satyrid butterfly discovers a receptive female, he flutters around her releasing alluring scent pheromones from his scent scales (androconia) which stimulate the female to copulate with him. (The female is the yellower of the two butterflies shown.) The marbled white is quite conspicuous when seen from above, but it is well camouflaged on the underside. The grey-green patches on a white background tend to break up its outline and enable it to merge effectively with the flowering spikelets of cock's foot and other grasses among which it rests. This species has a wingspan of 4.5-5.5cm ($1\frac{2}{3}$-$2\frac{1}{5}$in).

Above: A male speckled wood butterfly (*Pararge aegeria*). This species suffered a severe decline at the end of the last century but is now recovering.

Left: A male gatekeeper, or hedge brown, butterfly (*Pyronia tithonus*). This species, like the meadow brown and marbled white, can sometimes be found infested with tiny parasitic red mites. These suck the body fluid of the butterflies but unless the infestation is heavy do little real harm.

The spread of the speckled wood

- ■ up to 1910
- ■ 1911–1969
- ■ 1970–1980

The eye spots possibly serve a useful purpose in deflecting the attacks of predators (such as birds and lizards) away from the butterfly's body. The insect is perhaps most vulnerable when it first alights since an unseen enemy may be attracted by the movement of the butterfly and launch a sudden attack. By flashing its eye spots as it alights, the butterfly may well deflect the attack away from its body and escape with only the loss of part of one wing–not too great a handicap.

Therefore, when settling down to rest, a brown butterfly such as a meadow brown allows the conspicuous eye spot under the tip of each forewing to peep out above the otherwise camouflaged hind-wings. If no attack is forthcoming, it withdraws its forewings most entirely behind the hind-wings, co cealing the eye spot; the butterfly then rel for safety on camouflage that helps it merge with its surroundings.

Camouflage colouring The shade-lovi speckled wood, a truly woodland species, h evolved an ingenious camouflage in whi the irregular pattern of pale yellowish blotch on the dark, sooty brown wings renders almost invisible in dark foliage dappled w sunlight. Two generations of this butter occur each year, and fly from April October. When the first generation is on t wing in the spring, the tree canopy is natura more open than it is later in the summer a therefore allows larger shafts of sunlight penetrate the shade; the spring butterfl therefore have larger blotches on their win than the summer brood.

Territorial sparring Speckled wood mal defend patches of sunlit foliage against oth males which perch higher up in the canop The owner of the patch scent-marks h territory. Every now and then one of t surplus males descends to the sunlit patch a engages its occupant in 'battle'. They spir rapidly upwards until the intruder breaks the encounter and returns to the canopy. T original occupant of the patch almost alwa wins the dispute. Since females are al attracted to these sunny places, the occupyi males stand the best chance of mating wi them.

Nectar feeders The majority of brow butterflies visit a wide variety of flowers feed on the nectar which gives them energ for flight and mating; gatekeepers, meado browns and ringlets gather at bramble blo soms, while marbled whites are fond knapweed, scabious and thistle flower Speckled woods, however, are not often see feeding from flowers, preferring the hone dew from aphids which they take from le surfaces.

Life cycles The basic life-histories of th various browns have much in common wit each other. In Britain the browns a generally single brooded. However, in favou able years, partial second broods may produced by the meadow brown, while th speckled wood is always double brooded The caterpillars are all grass-feeders and with the partial exception of the speckle wood, pass the winter in this stage.

The eggs of the browns are generally mor or less spherical in shape with fine groove but may have flattened tops, like those c the gatekeeper and meadow brown. Th females lay their eggs on blades of grass except for the female marbled whites an ringlets which scatter theirs at random a they walk or fly over the grass.

The caterpillars have little difficulty i finding their foodplants on hatching, a though the caterpillars of the marbled whit do not feed until the end of winter, hibernat

Below: The speckled wood has a wingspan of 3.5-4.5cm (1⅛-1⅔in).

Speckled wood

Gatekeeper

Above: The gatekeeper has a wingspan of 3.5-4cm (1⅓-1½in).

Below: The meadow brown has a wingspan of 4.5-5cm (1⅔-2in).

Meadow brown

How to tell a butterfly from a moth

Most butterflies are brighter in colour than moths, although some moths are very colourful indeed. For instance, the burnet moth and the cinnabar moth are much brighter than the brown butterflies. Also, although most moths are night fliers, some fly by day, as do all butterflies. Therefore the time of day you see them is not always a good guide. The easiest way is to look at the antennae. Those of all European butterflies are clubbed at the tips—a feature never truly present in moths.

Most butterflies rest with their wings held above their backs, like the brown hairstreak (below left); moths, however, rest with their wings folded down, like the garden tiger moth (below right).

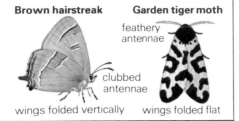

Brown hairstreak

clubbed antennae

wings folded vertically

Garden tiger moth

feathery antennae

wings folded flat

g in the meantime as tiny larvae. The precise species of grass consumed in the wild by the caterpillars of the different brown butterflies is not well known, although most of them to favour cock's foot grass and couch grass; the meadow brown especially likes smooth meadowgrass and the marbled white sheep's fescue.

Satyrid caterpillars have a soft velvety appearance due to the presence of numerous very small downy warts. Their spindle-shaped bodies tapering towards the hind end and terminating in a pair of sharp points are characteristic of the family. They are well camouflaged on their food plants, among which they usually hide during the day, coming out only at night to feed.

When the caterpillars are fully fed and ready to pupate in the autumn, most species, including the speckled wood, ringlet, gate-keeper and meadow brown, do so suspended upside down. A few, however, like the marbled white, simply lie loose on the ground among grass roots. The chrysalids, smooth, round and dumpy in shape, are also well camouflaged, usually being a shade of brown or green. Depending on the species, the adult butterflies emerge from the chrysalids in two to four weeks.

Widespread distribution All five of the species described here are mainly sedentary in habit, although apparently migratory movements of meadow browns are known.

Right: The meadow brown butterfly (*Maniola jurtina*) often swarms at the blossoms of brambles, seeking energy giving nectar. It sometimes flies in dull weather and occasionally even at night, when it may be attracted to bright lights.

Right: A meadow brown caterpillar. The pair of sharp points at the tail end were thought to resemble the pointed ears of a satyr (a woodland god)—hence the scientific name (Satyridae) of this family.

Below: A female ringlet butterfly (*Aphantopus hyperantus*); note the line of ringed eye spots. This species has a wingspan of 4-5cm (1½-2cm). Most browns fly in a jerky, rather feeble manner; you can usually see them flitting lazily from flower to flower or among grasses in the sunshine. The ringlet, like the meadow brown and speckled wood, is often active in dull weather, especially if it is rather sultry.

meadow brown caterpillar

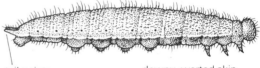

tail points   downy, warted skin

The meadow brown is probably the commonest and most widespread of all our British butterflies. It flies from June to September in open country, even on windswept islands, and haunts woodland rides and edges as well, which are also the chief habitat of the gatekeeper and the ringlet. The ringlet is especially fond of lush, grassy places but, like the gatekeeper, is often common among hedgerows in open countryside. Both these species fly in July and August. Although the ringlet is locally common in Scotland, the gatekeeper is virtually unknown there.

The speckled wood is also locally common in Scotland in the north-west, where it is represented by a distinct race. The typical race, which has recently been recovering lost ground in much of England following a serious decline at the end of the last century, is slowly spreading north and may eventually recolonize its former haunts in Scotland. Today the speckled wood is common in many parts of England, particularly in the south and west, and in Wales and Ireland.

The marbled white is typically a grassland butterfly, appearing especially on calcareous soils where it often forms distinct colonies. It flies in July and August over much of south-central England, especially the south-west where it is locally common. Although it has disappeared from many places in north-east England, colonies still survive in the Yorkshire wolds, and it occurs sporadically along the south coast of Wales.

JEWELS OF THE DOWNLANDS

The summer flowers of our chalk downlands support a group of distinctive blue butterflies. But this habitat is fast disappearing, taking the butterflies with it.

day in high summer on chalk downland, ...en the air is warm and scented with herbs ...owing in the close-grazed turf, is the ideal ...ne to look for blue butterflies. We have six ...ecies which frequent the chalk and lime-...ne downlands of southern England in ...mmer: the chalk-hill, Adonis, common, ...ver-studded, small and brown Argus.

It is the male butterflies which have the ...autiful blue colouring (with the exception of ...e brown Argus). The females are mainly ...own, with only slight traces of blue on their ...ngs. The underwing colouring in both sexes ... fairly similar, consisting of a pattern of ...hite-ringed black dots on a grey back-...ound. All species except the small blue also ...ve a yellow or orange underwing border.

Collectors' item The chalk-hill blue butter-... is now common in only a few places. A ...w in every hundred are variations—with an ...usual number of underwing spots, or spots ...tended into streaks. In the early part of ...is century, butterfly collectors were fascin-...ed by these variations and a book was ...ritten giving complicated names to every ...inor variation. Collectors eagerly awaited ...e emergence of the chalk-hill butterflies in ...te July and early August.

Surprisingly, it is not over-collecting which ...as led to the decline in chalk-hill numbers, ...ut the changes in the species' downland ...abitat. The eggs, laid in August, don't hatch ...ntil the next spring; when the caterpillars

Above: A male silver-studded blue butterfly, a species locally common on heaths and grassy downs in the south of England but absent from the north.

Opposite page: A common blue butterfly on bird's-foot trefoil.

Below: A caterpillar of a chalk-hill blue butterfly attended by an ant which is collecting the sweet secretion produced by the caterpillar.

emerge they feed on vetch—almost always a horsehoe vetch. This is a common plant on unploughed downland where the grass is grazed by sheep or rabbits. When rabbits became rarer after myxomatosis was introduced, many downs became dense thickets of thorny scrub. Other areas of downland were ploughed up and used for growing cereal crops. Both these changes eliminated the vetch—and the blue butterflies with it.

The brilliant Adonis blue is a very close relative of the chalk-hill. Its caterpillars feed on the same plants and are usually found in the same areas. Where they differ is that the Adonis blue has two generations a year. The first generation flies in May and June, the second in August and early September.

Very occasionally, a male of one species may mate with a female of the other species. The resulting hybrid is one of the few examples of hybridization occurring in natural conditions. The fact that this happens is good evidence for the close relationship of the two species.

Environment and ants A map of the distribution of both the chalk-hill and Adonis blue butterflies in Britain looks just like a map of our chalk and limestone downland areas. It seems that the butterflies need this type of soil, which gives a warm, dry, grassy area with vetches and plenty of ants.

The ants which live on downlands have a special relationship with the caterpillars of

Iridescence

Unlike such butterflies as the painted lady, the colour on a blue butterfly's wings is not produced by pigments. Its wing scales are built up of special transparent layers which directly alter or interfere with the way the light is reflected from them. The layers are at just the right distance apart to create the bright blue iridescent colour.

blue butterflies, and protect them from attack by ichneumon wasps which attempt to lay eggs inside the caterpillars. The caterpillars have a special gland on the tenth segment that secretes a sweet, honey-like substance which is most attractive to ants. The ants milk the caterpillars for this secretion, and in return move them round from food plant to food plant as necessary, often taking them nearer the ants' nests.

Contrasting trio You may find the remaining blue butterflies in other lowland habitats as well as on downland, depending on whether the right food plant is available.

The small blue—as its name suggests—is the smallest British butterfly. You'll always find its localised colonies in sheltered places—an old chalk pit for example. The caterpillars eat kidney vetch showing a special liking for flowers and developing seeds. They feed up quickly and start their long hibernation in the middle of summer. The pupa is formed in May and after two weeks in the chrysalis stage the butterflies hatch in late May or early June.

In contrast, the silver-studded blue is a butterfly of high summer, spending the winter in the egg stage. It is often found on sandy heaths where the caterpillars feed on heather and heath plants. The downland and coastal limestone races of this butterfly feed on rock-roses and plants of the pea family.

The common blue is well-named. It is not

restricted to chalky areas, and you can find almost anywhere in the British Isles where food plant, bird's-foot-trefoil, grows. In th south of England there are two overlappi generations, so the adult common blues in any month from May to September. In th north of England and in Scotland there is on one generation, and the adults are about June and July. It hibernates as an immatu caterpillar.

Odd-one-out It may seem odd to include th brown Argus with the blue butterflies sin both the males and the females of the speci are brown with orange spots. However, th pattern of spots on the underwing clear indicates this butterfly's relationship with th other blues. Also, the brown Argus's li cycle is similar, and the caterpillars have th typical squat, slug-like shape of the oth caterpillars.

Brown Argus caterpillars eat rock-rose an common stork's-bill flowers and freque sandy and coastal places as well as chalk areas. There is time in the longer summers the south for two generations of brown Argu butterflies to appear each year (like the com mon blue), but for only one generation in th colder north of England and Scotland. Th two types have now been distinguishe as different, but closely related, species. Th one-generation race is now known as th northern brown Argus. Both species hibe nate as immature caterpillars.

Chalk-hill blue

Common blue

Small blue

underwing

underwing

caterpillar

caterpillar

underwing

Chalk-hill blue
(Lysandra coridon)
has a wingspan of 30-35mm (1¼-1½in). The male is a light silvery blue with fairly broad black wing margin fringes. The female is brown. Absent from Ireland and Scotland.

Common blue
(Polyommatus icarus),
with a wingspan of 28-32mm (1-1¼in) has bright blue wings with a narrow white margin. The brown female has orange spots on the hind wing.

Common blue
caterpillar

Small blue (Cupido minimus), our smallest butterfly with a wingspan of 20-24mm (¾-1in), has very little blue colour. Only the male has any blue. Neither sex has orange underwing spots.

Left: Male and female brown Argus butterflies mating. This species over-winters in caterpillar form. All downland blue butterflies, except the small blue, have the noticeable yellow or orange underwing border.

Silver-studded blue
(Plebejus argus) has wingspan of 24-30mm (1-1¼in). Male is purple-blue in colour. Both male and female have a silver band on the hind wing underside, just inside a row of orange dots.

Brown Argus *(Aricia agestis),* with a wingspan of 24-28mm (1-1¼in), has no blue colouring at all. The orange spots on the upper wings may form a continuous band. Male and female are very similar in appearance.

caterpillar

Silver-studded blue

♀

underwing

♂

Adonis blue

underwing

♀

Brown Argus

caterpillar

♂

underwing

Adonis blue
(Lysandra bellargus) has a wingspan of 28-34mm (1¼-1½in). The male is very bright, shining blue with narrow white wing margins broken by black lines up the wings. Often active at night.

♀

Adonis blue

caterpillar

109

HOPPERS IN THE GRASS

Take a walk through a meadow in summer and you are bound to hear the chirpy, stridulating song made by the grasshopper.
It is a surprisingly loud sound for such a small creature.

Grasshoppers have two distinct characteristics: they jump and they sing. Jumping is achieved by the long powerful hind legs which are normally held in a sharply angled position and can be straightenend suddenly so as to hurl the grasshopper foward to a height and distance many times its own length; the grasshopper's small size saves it from being injured when it falls to earth again. As in most insects that have 'voices', singing is performed by stridulation – the scraping of a hard ridge on one part of the body over a series of closely set pegs or teeth on another part. Stroking your nail along a comb illustrates this very well.

Grasshoppers have fairly large eyes, short antennae, and hearing organs on each side of the base of the abdomen. Each 'ear' consists of a pressure-sensitive stretched membrane, called the tympanum, lying in a small pit.

Life in the grass Grasshoppers are well named for they all live among grass, and grass is their principal food. They lay their eggs enclosed in little packets called egg-pods, each one consisting of a fairly tough case and containing up to 14 eggs. Grasshoppers overwinter as eggs, and the pods serve to protect them during this long period.

Hatching usually takes place in April.

Above: Meadow grasshoppers (*Chorthippus parallelus*) mating. The males are usually smaller than the females, which are about 2cm ($\frac{3}{4}$in) in length. Like all British grasshoppers this species feeds on grass and is active in daylight; but unlike other species, it has vestigial wings and cannot fly. This species is widespread throughout the British Isles, with the exception of Ireland, the Isle of Man and some Scottish islands.

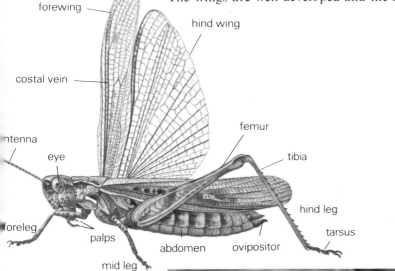

Grasshopper anatomy
Male and female grasshoppers can be distinguished by the shape of their abdomen tips (below). The male has a turned-up tip while the female's is straighter. The front pair of wings is thicker than the back.

male

female

forewing

hind wing

costal vein

femur

antenna

eye

tibia

hind leg

tarsus

foreleg

palps

abdomen ovipositor

mid leg

Right: A common green grasshopper (*Omocestus viridulus*); this is a female (you can tell by the shape of the tip of the abdomen). Females reach a length of 2cm (about ¾in). This is the only species that is common in high moorland areas as well as most lowland grassy habitats.

The young grasshopper, or nymph, is at first enclosed in a membraneous sac so that it looks like a small worm or grub. After wriggling out of the egg this worm-shaped (vermiform) larva sheds its skin and assumes the form of a minute wingless grasshopper. The nymph sheds its skin four more times before becoming an adult with fully developed wings.

Common grasshoppers There are only 11 species of grasshopper native to Britain, but they are not easy to distinguish. In all of them the coloration is more or less variable and is not a reliable guide to the species. They are therefore separated by reference to details in the form of the wings, thorax and antennae, and the number and spacing of the stridulatory pegs on the hind legs. If you have a good musical ear, the grasshopper's song is often the best clue to its identity. Females are usually a little larger than males.

The common green grasshopper is usually green above, with brown or purple sides, but there is also an all-brown variety of the male. The wings are well-developed and the males fly readily. The male has 100 to 140 stridulatory pegs on each hind leg.

This grasshopper lives in grassland where the vegetation is fairly thick and lush. The green variety of the male is commoner than the brown in moister, greener surroundings. It occurs all over the British Isles; in southern England nymphs first appear in April or May, rarely earlier. Adults are usually plentiful from July to September, when they begin to die off.

The normal song of the male is a prolonged and rapid ticking sound, each burst of song lasting 10 to 20 seconds or longer. In the presence of the female a much less regular song is produced.

The common field grasshopper is variable in colour, ranging from green and brown, pink and purple, to almost black, but the body is never wholly green above. The wings are well-developed, making it the best flyer of all our grasshoppers. It is also one of the largest. The male stridulatory organ consists of 50 to 90 pegs.

This is another common species, which prefers dry situations with exposed rock (or concrete) and is often seen on roadsides and among buildings. It is found all over the British Isles but is uncommon in the far north. The male sings in a series of six to ten short brisk chirps, each chirp lasting rather less than half a second. Two or more males together often chirp alternately at a higher tempo than that of a solitary male. There is no special courtship song, but the unmated females sing freely though less loudly than the males.

In the meadow grasshopper the wings are much reduced, the hind wings being vestigial in both sexes. The forewings of the female are shortened while those of the male barely reach the tip of the abdomen. Neither sex is

capable of sustained flight. Green, brown and purple varieties occur, and the male has 70 to 130 stridulatory pegs.

The meadow grasshopper is a little smaller than the common green. It is found in all kinds of grasslands throughout Great Britain, but does not extend to Ireland, where its absence may well be due to its inability to fly. Ireland was separated from Europe long before the English Channel was formed. Insects migrating north after the last Ice Age could easily reach England, but those that were unable to fly would not have been able to reach Ireland.

The male song is rather subdued and consists of little bursts of stridulation, each lasting from one to three seconds and spaced at three to fifteen-second intervals. The singing is a little more animated in the presence of a female.

Rarities The three species already described are common and widespread, but the stripe-winged grasshopper is confined to southern England. It is mainly green but varies considerably, often appearing distinctly striped when seen from above. The wings are well-developed and the male has 300 to 450 small stridulatory pegs. The song is distinctive, consisting of a continuous wheezy sound which lasts for about 10 to 20 seconds and is repeated at irregular intervals. In courtship the grasshopper alternates this sound with a subdued ticking.

Our largest and most exciting species is the large marsh grasshopper. It is distinguished by the colour of the hind legs: red on the inner surface of the femur, or on the thick basal half, and black and yellow towards the tip. Otherwise it is variously coloured dull green or brown. There are no stridulatory pegs on the legs of either sex. The male chirps by flicking the ends of his hind legs on to the tips of the wings, usually using one leg at a time. This is a rare insect, which is confined to wet bogs. Its occurrence in the British Isles is curious – a patchy distribution in southern England and the westernmost parts of Ireland. In particular it frequents areas where bog myrtle and bog asphodel grow. In England there is a colony in the New Forest.

Above: One of our rarer species of grasshopper, the stripe-winged (*Stenobothrus lineatus*); this species can be found in southern England on dry, chalky soils where the grass is fairly short.

Right: The large marsh grasshopper (*Stethophyma grossum*), our largest and rarest species. Females may measure up to 3.2cm (1$\frac{1}{4}$in). You'll find them only in wet bogs and fens; there is a well-known colony in the New Forest.

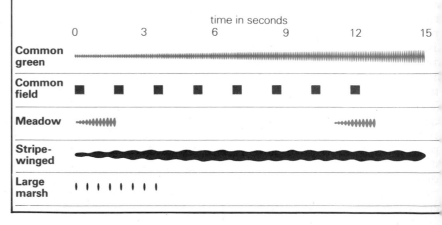

The grasshopper's song

If you watch a singing grasshopper, you'll see it making small movements with its legs. On the inner surface of the large thigh-joint there is a row of minute teeth or pegs which are pressed against the more prominent veins of the forewing on each side. The leg movements cause the wings to vibrate and produce the characteristic stridulating sound. This equipment is well-developed only in the males. Each species of male grasshopper has a specific song by which it can be recognised. Differences in 'voices' are determined by the number and spacing of the pegs.

Each song has been represented diagrammatically (below) by a horizontal pattern drawn parallel to a time scale in seconds. Each coloured mark denotes a sound; the spaces between each, silence. The width of each mark gives an indication of the loudness of the song.

inside right hind leg

stridulatory pegs

	time in seconds				
	0	3	6	9	12	15
Common green						
Common field						
Meadow						
Stripe-winged						
Large marsh						

SINGING CRICKETS

Bush-crickets, which live mainly in bushes and among moist, low-growing vegetation, are seldom seen, though their mating songs are heard frequently in the summer.

The insect order Orthoptera, meaning straight wings, includes the familiar grasshoppers and crickets as well as the less well-known bush-crickets. All of them are able to jump some distance with their strong hind legs, and the males of most species attract the females for mating purposes by making a noise called stridulation or, more colloquially, singing. This is produced by scraping together their legs and wings, or in the case of bush-crickets, just the wings. Each of our ten species of bush-cricket has its own character-istic sound, and the females only respond to sounds made by their own species.

Life-cycle In late summer or autumn, female bush-crickets use their strong oviposi-tors to place their eggs in crevices in plants or soil where they remain all through the winter. They hatch the following May or June to produce worm-like larvae that rapidly shed their skins to become nymphs. These look like tiny editions of the adults, but without wings or ovipositors. There is no pupal stage, the nymphs moulting several times until the last moult produces an adult.

Male adults have cerci, or pincer-like appendages, on the tip of their abdomen, instead of ovipositors. Some male adults have only short wings and in females they may be virtually absent, depending on the species.

Both nymphs and adults feed on a mixture of leaves and soft insects and it seems that

Above: A male great green bush-cricket (*Tettigonia viridissima*). Being a large and rather heavy insect, the flight of this bush-cricket is poor, despite its long wings, and usually lasts for only a few metres.

Below: An older nymph of the great green bush-cricket, distinguished from the short-winged adults of some species by its wing pads, which are reversed, with the leading edge uppermost. In adults the leading edge is downwards.

Cricket v grasshopper

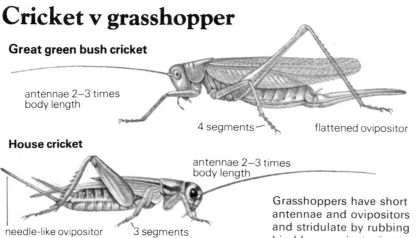

Great green bush cricket

antennae 2–3 times body length

4 segments

flattened ovipositor

House cricket

antennae 2–3 times body length

needle-like ovipositor

3 segments

Common field grasshopper

short antennae

short ovipositor

Grasshoppers have short antennae and ovipositors and stridulate by rubbing hind legs against wings. Crickets have a needle-like ovipositor, 3-segmented tarsi and long antennae. Bush-crickets have a flattened ovipositor, long antennae and 4-segmented tarsi. Both types of cricket stridulate with wings only.

in suburban avenues for crevices in which place her eggs. The adults, which appear August and are comparatively long-lived, frequently attracted to artificial light and m be found around house lights even in la November.

Oak bush-crickets are attractive inse with a fragile, delicate appearance, so that is rather a surprise to find that, alone amo the species, they are almost complet carnivorous. Their diet consists for the ma part of small caterpillars, aphids and oth soft-bodied insects.

Small and speckled The speckled bus cricket, a bright green insect with numero tiny brown spots, is another small speci measuring only 9-17mm ($\frac{3}{8}$-$\frac{3}{4}$in) long. T adults can be found in August and Septemb in gardens, and on bushes and brambles open woodland. They are mainly found in t southern half of England, but have also be recorded from Wales, Ireland and weste Scotland.

Speckled bush-crickets are flightless, ha

at least some animal food is essential.

Green 'giant' The great green bush-cricket is our largest species. It is found in parts of southern England and Wales and may be quite common in warm southern coastal districts, the adults appearing from late July to September.

Measuring up to 5.5cm ($2\frac{1}{4}$in) long, it is found on rough, shrubby land, where there is plenty of cover provided by nettles, thistles or reeds. It is mainly green in colour, but with a dark brown stripe down the back. The female's ovipositor, which is sword-like and nearly straight, measures up to 2.2cm ($\frac{7}{8}$in) long and she lays a total of about 200 eggs in crevices in the soil.

Like many other bush-crickets, this species lives in colonies and seldom flies or hops, preferring to run quickly down into the undergrowth if disturbed. During the afternoon and evening the males can be seen when they climb to the tops of thistles or bushes and stridulate very loudly. They produce a harsh, high-pitched sound which is more or less continuous and carries for 200m (220 yards) or more.

Tree-dweller The oak bush-cricket, most frequently seen in London suburban gardens and tree-lined avenues, is a much smaller, pale green insect, measuring 14-17mm ($\frac{1}{2}$-$\frac{3}{4}$in) in length. It is the only British species that normally lives in trees and, in spite of its name, it is found in lime, apple, maple and lilac trees and not just oak. It is quite common in deciduous woods in England, south of the Humber, and in Wales and has also been recorded from Ireland and the Lake District.

Mainly a nocturnal insect, it prefers to walk rather than jump or fly, despite its well-developed wings. The ovipositor is fairly long and curves upwards and the female may be seen at dusk, probing the bark of tree trunks

Left: A male and a larger female bog bush-cricket. There are brown and green colour forms of this species the green form shown here is the more common.

Below: Most species of bush-cricket, like the dark bush-cricket (*Pholidoptera griseoaptera*) shown here, supplement their diet of a variety of leaves with any soft-bodied insects that the can catch.

Sound production and hearing

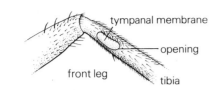

Male bush-crickets stridulate by scraping a thickened, tooth-bearing vein at the base of the left forewing against the thickened hind edge of the right forewing. At the base of the latter a small area, known as the mirror, acts as a resonator. Stridulation, which is usually high-pitched, can be a series of short chirps or a much longer, continuous song. The purpose of the song is to attract females for mating. Hearing organs are visible as slit-like openings in the tibiae of the front legs of both sexes. They contain a tympanal membrane which picks up sound, as do our ears.

Above: The flightless female speckled bush-cricket (*Leptophyes punctatissima*) can be identified by her virtual lack of wings and broad, upturned ovipositor.

Above: Nymphs of bush-crickets are small versions of the adults, without the wings or ovipositors which do not appear until they have moulted about five times. When rudimentary wing pads and ovipositors appear, they continue to grow until the last moult, which produces the adult; there is no pupal stage. However, in nymphs of flightless species, like the dark bush-crickets shown here, only vestiges of wings develop. Nymphs take about three months to mature—these would be adult by August.

g no hind wings and forewings that are reduced to small brown flaps in the male, and virtually nothing in the female. The antennae and hind legs are unusually long, however; this species seems to hop more than the others. There is just enough of the males' forewings remaining for stridulating and they are able to produce short chirps every few seconds, although this is a faint sound and hardly audible more than 1 metre (39in) away.

The female has a short, broad, curved ovipositor. She places her eggs, which are unusual in being thin and oval in outline, in plant stems and bark crevices.

A common cricket The medium-sized dark bush-cricket, which measures 13-20mm (½-in) long, is probably the commonest of the British species in England. It appears south of North Yorkshire and also in south Wales, but is not recorded from Scotland or Ireland.

It is another flightless species, with no hind wings and only just sufficient of the male's forewings remaining for stridulation. In the female, there are only vestiges of the forewings remaining.

Dark bush-crickets are most commonly found in colonies in nettle-beds, brambles and herbage alongside roads or woods—in fact, almost anywhere with sufficient cover and some light. They seem to be the least particular species in their choice of habitat, although they are not found in open fields and heaths. They sometimes even find their way into houses in the evenings.

The predominant colour of this species is brown to almost black, with a yellow underside to the abdomen. The dark colour and rather long hind legs give it a somewhat spidery appearance. The ovipositor of the female is 10mm (⅜in) long, pointed and curved upwards. She lays her eggs in crevices in bark or rotten wood. In common with the other species the eggs overwinter, but they are the earliest to hatch, from late April onwards. The adults appear towards the end of July and live until October or even November.

The males produce a brisk chirping sound, with a few seconds between each chirp and although they do this for most of the day, there is an increase in the evening. They are difficult insects to see or catch, due to their choice of shrubby or prickly cover. If disturbed, they immediately jump or crawl downwards, camouflaged by their colour.

Moorland species Most of the remaining six species are rare or uncommon, but the bog bush-cricket (*Metrioptera brachypetra*) deserves a mention as it is frequent on the moister areas of heathland and moors from southern Scotland, throughout England and Wales. In size, appearance and its brownish colour it resembles the dark bush-cricket, but the underside of the abdomen is green and there is a broad, pale band along the side flaps of the thorax. The best way to distinguish the two species is by their song which, in the bog bush-cricket consists of a continuous series of shrill chirps, without the pauses of the dark bush-cricket's song, which may last for several minutes at a time.

BUMBLE BEES—A BUSY LIFE

The life cycle of bumble bees is squeezed into a few short months; all the members of a colony (begun by a single queen in spring) die in autumn except new queens, which hibernate.

Bumble bees, like honey bees and ants, are social insects and live together in colonies; unlike those of the other two, however, bumble bees' colonies are annual ones, newly built each year. Bumble bees do not store honey to tide them over winter, so in autumn all members of the colony die except the young mated queens which hibernate until spring in the shelter of a hedgerow, heap of moss or pile of leaves, normally burrowing a few inches below the surface of the soil. The rest of the life cycle is squeezed into our few spring and summer months.

Building a nest In early spring you can often see a queen bumble bee, newly emerged from hibernation, blundering around close to the ground as if she were looking for something. What she is searching for is a suitable place to nest. Some species choose underground sites—a leaf-filled hole beneath the roots of a decaying tree, or a disused hedgehog or mouse nest—while others, the carder bees, make an above-ground, ball-shaped nest of moss, grass and leaves which they weave or 'card' together.

Once the nesting site is established, the queen makes a circular chamber, about 3cm (1¼in) in diameter, in the centre and dries it out with the warmth of her own body. She lines the chamber with a layer of wax produced from special glands on the underside of her abdomen, then makes a cell to receive the eggs which have developed inside her from

her mating the previous autumn. The cup-shaped cell is moulded out of a mixture of wax and pollen and is filled with yet more pollen. Finally the queen lays ten or more eggs inside the cell and seals it with a lid of wax.

The queen bumble bee is a careful and provident mother; she incubates her eggs by sitting on the cell to keep it warm, and also continues to search for food. She brings in more nectar and pollen—the sole food of adult and larvae—than she herself needs and stores them in a specially constructed 'honey-pot' made from wax so that her brood will not go short when cold, wet weather confines her to the nest.

Moss carder bee with laden pollen baskets. Bumble bees get their name from their slow bumbling flight; the body looks too heavy for the small wings, but the thrust and lift achieved by the way the wings beat are more than enough to lift the bee and its load. The wings twist on every stroke, are clapped together at the top of the up-stroke, and are then opened rapidly, so creating vortex which increases the lift on the next down-stroke.

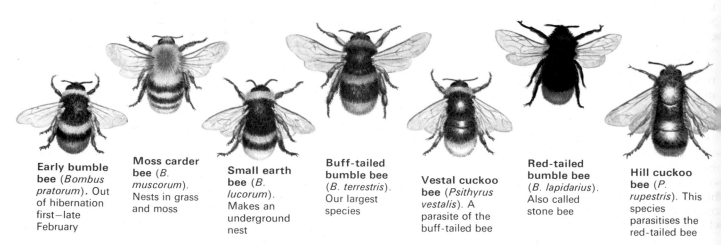

Early bumble bee (*Bombus pratorum*). Out of hibernation first—late February

Moss carder bee (*B. muscorum*). Nests in grass and moss

Small earth bee (*B. lucorum*). Makes an underground nest

Buff-tailed bumble bee (*B. terrestris*). Our largest species

Vestal cuckoo bee (*Psithyrus vestalis*). A parasite of the buff-tailed bee

Red-tailed bumble bee (*B. lapidarius*). Also called stone bee

Hill cuckoo bee (*P. rupestris*). This species parasitises the red-tailed bee

Looking inside a bumble bee nest

The above-ground nest of the common carder bee (*Bombus agrorum*) is lined with wax to keep out the damp, and completely surrounded with a cover of moss and grass skilfully plaited or 'carded' together. The queen leaves a flight hole open so that she, and later on her workers, can come and go with ease. This nest has been opened to show the interior: the brown (wax-covered) cells contain larvae while the yellow (silk-covered) ones hold pupae. At the bottom of the picture there are a couple of wax 'honey pots' which are used to store food to tide the colony over when it's too cold and wet for the workers to go out.

The growing colony The larvae – which look like white grubs – hatch in about five days and feed on the pollen provided in their cell. The queen replenishes the cell at intervals with regurgitated nectar and pollen and the larvae grow quickly on the rich diet. They moult several times, then spin silken cocoons around themselves and pupate inside them. At this stage, the queen removes the wax round the cocoons and uses it to build new cells. After about two weeks the very small adults – all unfertilized, subordinate females – gnaw their way out of the cocoons. They are the workers whose job in life is to keep the queen and her growing colony supplied with food and to defend the nest and assist with cell-building. They never mate but they can lay eggs which, since they are not fertilized, produce only males (drones).

While the workers forage, the queen stays in the nest, building new cells and laying more eggs. Eventually a colony of up to several hundred workers may develop. The cluster of cells – the comb – is rarely larger than the palm of a man's hand; as the food supply increases and the nest is enlarged, the workers also increase in size.

Towards the end of summer, the queen lays a number of unfertilized eggs which develop into drones; their sole task is to mate with the queens – they never work. At the same time, the fertilized eggs the queen lays develop not into workers but into new queens – up to 200 in large nests. These larvae are fed by numerous workers and receive an abundance of food; it is this level of nutrition which determines whether fertilized eggs become workers or queens.

In late summer the young queens and drones disperse to find mates from other colonies. By late autumn the old queen, workers and drones have all died and only the young fertilized queens go into hibernation.

Collecting food Neither queen nor worker bumble bee needs to be taught how to go about gathering food; they instinctively know what to look for. Their long tongues enable them to reach the nectar stored deep inside long-throated flowers such as foxglove and white dead-nettle, while the hairs on their bodies brush masses of pollen from the flower stamens. You can sometimes see bumble bees almost completely covered in a dusting of pollen. The pollen is held by special storage 'baskets' on the bee's back legs – some bees are known to have carried up to 60% of their own weight in pollen, but a more usual load is 20%. The humming or buzzing you can hear as the bees fly from flower to flower is produced by the vibration of the wings which beat incredibly fast, at a rate of 130 to 240 beats per second according to the size of the bee (smaller bees have faster wing beats). The workers, which usually live for several weeks, go out to forage every day except when it is cold and rainy.

Cuckoo bees

Bumble bees are parasitised by cuckoo bees which look like their hosts but are less hairy and have no pollen baskets. The female cuckoo bee invades the nest, kills the queen, then lays her own eggs. These are cared for by the workers and develop into queens and drones (never workers) which are unable to collect pollen. Alien drones die in autumn, but the fertilized queens hibernate until the next spring when they emerge to take over another bumble bee nest.

How a bee collects nectar

the proboscis is folded into a groove under the head when the bee is not feeding

hairy tongue —

the proboscis is composed of several moveable parts enclosing the hairy tongue (the glossa)

To drink nectar, the bee brings forward its proboscis and alternately shortens and lengthens its tongue. Nectar is drawn up by capillary action through a deep channel enclosed by the hairs on the tongue and passes to the honey stomach, where it is stored until the bee returns to its nest.

Collecting pollen

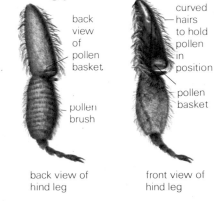

back view of pollen basket

pollen brush

back view of hind leg

curved hairs to hold pollen in position

pollen basket

front view of hind leg

The female bumble bee and honey bee (but not the cuckoo bee) collect pollen to take back to the nest. Using her front and middle legs, a bee brushes pollen off the hairs on her head and front part of her body forwards to her mouth. She moistens the pollen with nectar and then passes it to the pollen brush on one hind leg and finally to the pollen basket of the opposite hind leg. It is then pressed into position and held in the basket by the fringe of long, curved hairs.

THE SECRET LIFE OF MEADOW ANTS

The mounds which appear all over fields and meadows house the nests of the yellow meadow ant and are often the only evidence of their presence. Rarely seen on the surface, these ants have an underground life which they share with a variety of creatures.

Below: Distinctive yellow meadow ant mounds. If the mound is soft and crumbly at the top then the ants are present and building; if it is hard, you can be reasonably sure the nest is deserted.

Some country people still speak of 'emmet casts', 'emmet' being the archaic English word for ant. 'Emmet casts' are the distinctive large mounds produced in uncultivated fields by the yellow ant. This species is also sometimes known as the yellow hill ant or the common yellow ant.

Meadow mounds The mounds of the yellow meadow ant are usually rounded or slightly elongated in shape. The old ones may be a metre or so in height and must be levelled if hay is to be cut or grown in a field. They usually have a long slope up to the highest point and then a steeper slope, which faces east or south-east. The ants live in, and continue building, the mound at the eastern end, possibly because of the combination of warm sun and morning dew that they find when they come to the surface.

Although their mounds are a nuisance in haymaking and other mechanical farming operations, ants improve the quality of pasture by aeration and by mixing the soil which they bring to the surface from depths of a metre or more. In sandy soil or on steep slopes the yellow meadow ant does not make a mound at all. This is also true in gardens where cultivation, mowing and rolling of lawns prevents mound formation but does not destroy the subsurface nests.

Hierarchy in the nest In the meadow ant nest the average population of workers is around 10,000, but may reach over 20,000; there is usually only one queen. The workers, which seldom see the light, have poorly developed compound eyes compared with those ant species that live and work in the daylight.

A queen ant mates only once, after which she may lay many thousands of eggs. If she fertilises an egg before it is laid, using one of the thousands of sperms stored in her body, it will produce a female – either a worker or

Above: The large queen yellow meadow ant sheds her wings almost at once after mating.

t: Winged males and
eens, shown here with the
ngless workers, swarm
m the nest during settled
ather in late summer.
ey mate in the air, then
e queens descend to the
und. Only a very few
cceed in founding a nest
finding their way into an
sting nest, and most
rish.

jht: If a meadow ant nest
opened in summer, larvae
d pupae can be found in
antity. The larvae are
le white grubs whose
e varies with age. The
pae are contained in oval
coons, those of the males
d queen being larger. The
coons resemble very large
gs, and are as big as the
ts themselves.

low: Yellow meadow ant
orkers are very small,
easuring only 2-5mm.
ey are sometimes
nfused with common red
t workers, which
casionally make their
sts in a part of the mound
a yellow meadow ant
lony. However, red ant
orkers are larger and
rker, with a pair of
ckward-pointing spines on
e hind part of the thorax.
amination of the pupae
so helps to distinguish the
ecies—yellow meadow ant
pae are contained in
cocoons, while those of the
d ant are naked.

ommon red ant worker
(*Myrmica ruginodis*).

Yellow meadow ant
worker (*Lasius flavus*).

another queen. She can, however, withhold sperm altogether and the unfertilised egg will then develop into a male. This is the only way that males can be produced – a curious method of sex control that operates in all ants, wasps and bees.

Other nest-dwellers Many kinds of ants tend aphids in order to feed on their liquid excretions, which consist mainly of sugar and water derived from the plant sap on which the aphids exist.

The yellow meadow ants, which live almost entirely underground, compensate for their inability to tend aphids in the open by keeping special kinds of aphids in their own nest, pasturing them on the roots of plants that grow on the nest's surface. *Trama troglodytes*, a large, hairy aphid associated with plants of the daisy family, is found frequently in the nests of the yellow meadow ant, while *Forda formicaria*, a white or pale brown aphid, is virtually confined to ants' nests where it can be found singly or in little clusters on roots.

Another kind of insect attended by ants for the sake of their palatable secretions are the caterpillars of some of the blue butterflies.

The yellow meadow ant tends the caterpillars of the chalk-hill blue butterfly, carrying them around, placing them on plants near their nests and even protecting them with soil.

Ant guests Some small animals live in ants' nests, apparently as tolerated guests. One of these is the small white woodlouse (*Platyarthrus hoffmannseggi*), which is only found in the nests of a number of ant species, including the yellow meadow ant. It seems to feed on rejected pellets of indigestible matter and the ants take no notice of it at all.

Another guest with similar status and habits is the springtail. It is a tiny white insect, but conspicuous when a mound is opened up since it jumps actively about.

Finally, there is a curious relationship between yellow meadow ants and rabbits. The mounds attract rabbits, partly as vantage points and partly because they are comfortably warm to sit on as they catch the rays of the sun! The rabbits scatter pellets of dung on the mounds, enriching the grass and herbs growing there, to the advantage of the root-feeding aphids and of the ants which harbour them as an important source of food.

Underground 'farming'

The aphids kept underground by the yellow meadow ants seem to lead a secure existence, protected from the extremes of weather, and also from predators and parasites. Furthermore, the ants treat the aphids' eggs as they do their own, carrying them around and licking them to keep them free of moulds. Their lives are not, however, as carefree as this suggests. Besides milking them, the ants frequently kill and eat them to supplement their diet of various underground insects. The aphids' situation is thus very similar to that of cattle kept by man for both dairy produce and meat.

INSECT LIFE IN A LEAF

The pale blotches and wavy lines you find on many leaves are the tunnels, or mines, of tiny larval insects that make their homes between the upper and lower leaf surfaces.

A typical leaf is less than one millimetre thick and there is little room for any creature to move about between its upper and lower surfaces, but a large number of insects have been able to exploit this cramped space and its rich supply of food. These insects are the leaf miners. Most are moths and flies, although there are also some leaf-mining beetles and sawflies. All are, of course, very small insects.

The mines are always made by the larvae, most of which, through leading the same kind of life, have come to look very much alike. They tend to be colourless and legless, and the head tapers towards the front with the mouthparts right at the tip. The body is usually extremely flat—as you would expect of a creature living in a 'room' only a fraction of a millimetre high—although fly larvae are essentially cylindrical and merely become compressed as they tunnel through the leaf tissues.

Serpentine and blotch mines There are two main types of mine—the serpentine and the blotch. The serpentine mine is a sinuous tunnel which snakes its way through the leaf tissues. It is usually the work of a single larva and it generally gets progressively wider as the insect grows. Although it often starts near the edge of a leaf, the serpentine mine may begin at any point, but it rarely crosses the mid-rib of the leaf.

A blotch mine is formed when the larva excavates a relatively broad and often irregular area of the leaf. It may be the work of one or several larvae. Blotch mine occupants may make a little more room for themselves by spinning silken threads just inside the epidermis: the threads shrink as they dry and cause the surface to buckle, thus forming a slightly deeper chamber. Some species start off by making a linear mine and then gradually open it out to form a blotch. The beech leaf miner (*Rhynchaenus fagi*) is a good example. This is a small, greyish weevil and its larval mine begins near the mid-rib of the leaf and extends outwards to form the blotch close to the leaf margin.

Permanent and temporary homes Most leaf miners spend their entire larval life within a single mine, but some species mine only during their very early stages and then feed externally on the leaves. Most miners are unable to begin again once they have left their mines, but a number of species do leave their tunnels from time to time and begin new ones elsewhere—on the same leaf or on new leaves.

Pupation can take place inside the mine, although most species leave and pupate elsewhere. It is not always easy to see the hole through which a miner has left, but you can see if it is still at home by holding the leaf to the light. If the larva is still there, you may even be able to watch it feeding, relentlessly scraping away at the tissue.

Brambles and birches One of our commonest and most conspicuous leaf mines is that of the moth *Nepticula aurella*; the mines can be found on brambles almost everywhere. The serpentine mine shows up silvery grey or pale brown on the upper surface of the leaf. It normally starts as a thin tunnel near the edge of the leaf and is often very twisty in the early stages. The final length may be quite straight, often running alongside the mid-rib. The mines can be found at all times of the year, for the larva feeds through the winter. Prolonged frost kills it, however, so it is not found in places with severe winters. The adult moth has a wingspan of only 6mm ($\frac{1}{4}$in) but is beautifully patterned with purple and gold.

Adult leaf miners either lay their eggs on the surface of leaf or insert them into the tissues; the larvae begin mining as soon as they hatch. If the eggs are laid on the leaf surface the grubs usually emerge from the base of the egg and go straight into the leaf. The rich photosynthetic tissues of the leaf provide abundant nourishment for the small leaf-mining grubs, (such as the fly larvae shown here). Some species chew their way through the upper layers, just under the upper skin, while others prefer the lower layers. The pale mine, indicating where the tissues have been removed, can be seen on either surface, according to the insect species that makes it.

A few species mine the whole thickness of the leaf. The outer skin is usually left untouched, thus providing protection from desiccation and also from some enemies. Birds, however, frequently attack leaf mines and extract the insects, and parasites also take a heavy toll.

Birch leaves, especially those of young [tre]es, are commonly mined by the larvae of [an]other little moth called *Eriocrania semi-[pu]rpurella*. Almost every leaf may be affected [in] small trees. The mine is a pale blotch and [i]s occupied from late March to May. The [ex]crement, or frass, is bound up into long [int]er-twining threads, which immediately [id]entify the mine as belonging to the *Erio-[cra]nia*. The insect spends the winter in the [soi]l as a pupa.

Mining flies Few holly trees escape the [att]entions of *Phytomyza ilicis*, a tiny grey fly [wh]ose larvae produce yellowish blotch mines [of] a very irregular shape. These mines have a [bli]ster-like appearance. The insect is so [ab]undant at times that more than a third of the [lea]ves on a holly tree may be affected.

Dock leaves are commonly mined by flies [of] the genus *Pegomya*, of which *P. calyptrata* [is] a common example. The eggs are laid in [ba]tches and the larvae live communally in [blo]tch mines, which are often so extensive [th]at they link up and cover the whole leaf. [Th]e fully-grown larvae emerge through the [sh]rivelled upper epidermis and pupate in [th]e ground. The adults are like small house-[fli]es, with a bluish-grey thorax and an orange [ab]domen.

The jerking disc sawfly The leaves of [sy]camore and field maple often bear the pale [br]own blotch mines of *Heterarthrus aceris*. [T]here may be several mines in one leaf, [us]ually towards the extremities, but there is [ju]st one larva to each mine. The larvae feed [in] June and July, and when fully grown each [on]e cuts a perfectly circular disc from the [u]pper epidermis. A sheet of silk is spun on [th]e underside of the disc and the larva [sn]uggles down in this envelope. The whole [di]sc then falls from the leaf and the larva [sp]ends the next six months or so at rest.

It needs a moist, shady situation and so [an]y larva whose disc falls into a dry place [be]comes restless and throws its body from [on]e side of its case to the other. These move-[m]ents cause the whole disc to jerk about and [it] eventually comes to rest in a suitable spot. [T]he insect finally pupates in the envelope in [th]e spring and the adult emerges in May.

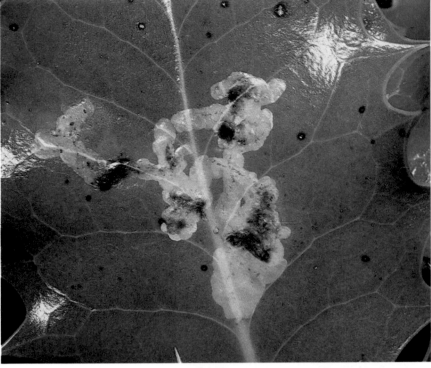

Blotch mine (above) made in a holly leaf by the fly *Phytomyza ilicis*, and serpentine mine (right) made by the moth *Nepticula aurella*. Many trees and shrubs are attacked by leaf miners, but the mines seem to have little effect on their general well-being unless they are particularly numerous. Frass is no problem in a serpentine mine, for it is simply left behind as the insect tunnels forward. The trail of frass can, in fact, identify the mine. Blotch miners sometimes make small flap-like openings in the leaf surface through which they jettison the frass, but most species simply leave it in the centre as they mine outwards. Some even bind the frass into little parcels with silk.

Jerking disc sawfly *Heterarthrus aceris*; larvae make blotch mines in sycamore.

Fly *Phytomyza ilicis*; larvae make blotch mines in holly leaves. Very abundant.

Fly *Pegomya calyptrata*; larvae make blotch mines in dock and live in extensive communities.

Moth *Nepticula aurella*; larvae make serpentine mines in bramble leaves.

Moth *Eriocrania semipurpurella*; larvae make pale blotch mines in leaves of birch.

Weevil *Rhynchaenus fagi*; larva starts with serpentine mine, widening to blotch, in beech.

SCAVENGING DUNG BEETLES

Dung beetles play a vital role in the ecology of the countryside by removing manure and burying it in the ground for their larvae to feed on. The adults and the larvae have enormous appetites, often eating their own weight of dung in one day.

Above: The dor beetle (*Geotrupes stercorarius*) unfurling its wings before take-off. Large numbers of these beetles can be seen swarming over cattle pastures on summer evenings, frequently crashing into cattle—manoeuvrability is one of their weaker points. They are sometimes called 'lousy watchmen' since they can be infested with brown mites (seen above on the beetle's abdomen), and because they fly in the early evening—when night watchmen go on their rounds.

It certainly cannot be said that dung beetles have the most charming of habits, yet their importance as scavengers must not be denied. In conjunction with numerous flies, they play a major part in the removal of mammal dung, particularly that of the larger herbivores—so much so that without them a large part of our countryside would disappear under a blanket of cowpats. In Australia, where there are no native dung beetles to clear up after the millions of introduced sheep and cattle, this has indeed become a major problem.

Several kinds of beetles and larvae are found in animal manure, but the true dung beetles belong to the group known as the lamellicorns (a name which refers to the

cluster of flaps—lamellae—at the tip of ea antenna). Within the lamellicorn group Br ish dung beetles fall into two families—t Geotrupidae (dor beetle, wood dor and min taur), in which the jaws are clearly visible fro above, and the Scarabaeidae (English scara in which the jaws are concealed.

Excavating a dung store One of our larg and most familiar dung beetles is the d beetle which, at 16-25mm ($\frac{2}{3}$-1in) long, is shiny black with a bright metallic blue green underside. It is associated mainly wi cow dung and is usually seen flying ov cattle pastures on summer evenings.

Mated pairs stay together and work as team when they find a suitable cowpat. T adults squeeze the food—which is main fluid—out of the dung with their jaws and th bury the bulk of the cowpat, usually at nig to provide sustenance for the larvae. T female uses her front legs and her large jaws dig a shaft (up to 60cm/2ft deep) under t dung, and then excavates a number of ov chambers. The male helps to remove the s and brings bundles of dung into the chambe

Food for the young The female lays an egg each chamber and then both adults leav Each chamber contains sufficient dung for t fleshy, white, C-shaped larva to complete growth during the next few months. The lar pupates in the surrounding soil and the ne adult emerges during the following year.

By burying the dung, the dor beetle e

Armed for battle

Several of our dung beetles—notably the English scarab and the minotaur (above)—have horns on the head or thorax. The horns are always larger in the males, some females having none at all, but no British species have horns which reach the sizes found in some tropical dung beetles. The main function of the horns appears to be fighting between rivals, the males waging battle with one another in much the same way as stags. Horn growth is linked to the amount of work done by the male—the less they work, the larger their horns.

The dung larder

The minotaur beetle, in common with many dung beetles, excavates a burrow in which to store food (dung) for its larvae. The burrow, built entirely by the female, comprises several chambers. The English scarab however, has only one chamber in its burrow, which both adults excavate. The male transports dung pellets to the chamber while the female moulds them into a rough sphere. After a few days she breaks this up and forms 'brood balls', into each of which she lays a single egg, finally sealing them with more dung. When the eggs hatch and develop into larvae there is enough food to last until they are fully grown.

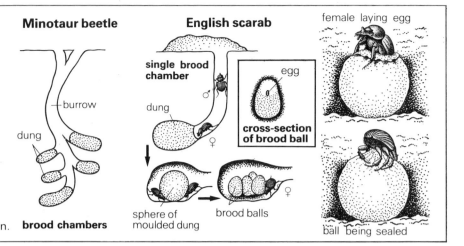

Minotaur beetle — burrow, dung, **brood chambers**

English scarab — single brood chamber, dung, cross-section of brood ball, egg, sphere of moulded dung, brood balls

female laying egg — ball being sealed

res that the manure does not dry out before e larvae have completed their growth. It so guarantees them a certain amount of otection from their enemies, although they e not completely safe even then. A smaller ing beetle, *Aphodius porcus*, sometimes in- des the dor beetle's burrow, destroying the gs and laying its own in the ready-stocked ambers.

Wood dor beetle The dor beetle has several ose relatives, including the extremely com- on wood dor beetle (*Geotrupes stercorosus*). his is similar to the dor beetle, but only 2-19mm ($\frac{1}{2}$-$\frac{3}{4}$in) long, and it often has wing ses showing a green, blue or purple idescence.

It occurs in many habitats but seems to refer woodland, where it may be found on otting fungi as well as dung. Its life history is e same as that of the dor beetle.

Bull-like beetle The minotaur beetle (*Typh- us typhoeus*) derives its name from the ale's two horn-like processes which point orward from the thorax. There is also a third omewhat smaller horn between the two lar- er ones. The female has virtually no horns nd rarely exceeds 15mm ($\frac{1}{2}$in) in length, hereas the male commonly reaches 20mm in). Both sexes are normally glossy black.

The minotaur is found mainly in southern ngland and Wales, usually on sandy ground, nd can be seen at most times of the year. warming may occur on warm evenings, specially in autumn, which is the main reeding season, but otherwise the beetle pends most of its time on or under the round. It feeds mainly on rabbit droppings ut occasionally turns to deer or sheep dung.

As in dor beetles, the dung is buried as food or the larvae, but the shaft is not necessarily unk close to the dung. The female does all he digging, the male's horns saving him from his arduous task. He does, however, scoop ut much of the excavated soil, and brings in ost of the food, often guiding the rabbit roppings with his horns.

The male also defends the burrow, sitting n the entrance with his horns projecting vhile his mate excavates. Any other males oming too near the burrow or trying to steal

a pellet of dung are attacked, the horns of the combatants clashing together in battle until the weaker male beats a hasty retreat.

Our native scarab The only scarab beetle we have in Britain is the English scarab (*Copris lunaris*). Black and shiny, sometimes with a brownish tinge, it is 15-20mm ($\frac{1}{2}$-$\frac{3}{4}$in) long and easily recognised by the single horn standing erect in the middle of its head. Both sexes are horned, although the female's horn is smaller than that of the male.

This species is quite rare in Britain, being confined to certain localities in southern and central England, normally on sandy soil. It is associated mainly with cattle dung and can be found from May to September.

Above: All the larger British species of dung beetles excavate burrows in which to store dung for their larvae to feed on.

Left: The wood dor beetle (*Geotrupes stercorosus*) prefers woodland habitats, where it invades dung and rotting fungi.

Below: The English scarab (*Copris lunaris*), at 15-20mm ($\frac{1}{2}$-$\frac{3}{4}$in long), is identifiable by the single horn which stands erect in the middle of its head.

Below: This dor beetle, in common with all other dung beetles, has large spiky front legs which resemble rakes, and are used to dig through the dung and excavate burrows.

Birds of field and hedgerow

For birds our miscellaneous composition of hedge, copse, field and woodland edge offers a greater variety of opportunities than large expanses of more uniform vegetation types. Many bird species whose traditional haunts are pure woodland or meadow successfully colonize these 'suburbs', producing a cosmopolitan community of surprising diversity. Some birds, such as wrens and dunnocks, exist at much higher densities in these fragments than they do in the primeval forest from which they originated. Fringe habitats may also be a compromise for species unable to establish themselves in proper woodland. For instance, many young great tits, outdone for prime woodland sites, set up territories in hedgerows.

The patchwork landscape provides ideal conditions for communication between birds. This is at a premium in the breeding season when many songsters seek a lofty outpost, with a good all-round view, from which to attract potential mates and to proclaim their territorial rights to rivals. Open ground, punctuated by hedgerow, scrub and scattered trees, offers the perfect arena for these vocal contests.

Such surroundings are also generous in their provision of food and shelter. Many of the typical shrubs and herbage bear flowers which attract insects, followed later in the year by rich pickings of seeds, nuts and berries. This allows a diversity of birds with different food preferences to coexist harmoniously in appreciable numbers. Open ground is also always within easy reach of cover, yielding more insects and invertebrates and harbouring voles and mice to sustain owls and kestrels.

The capacity of this habitat to support bird life is underlined by the fact that it can absorb a huge influx of migrants—whitethroats, garden warblers, blackcaps and cuckoos in the summer and berry-seeking redwings and fieldfares from northern Europe and beyond in autumn. As winter approaches, unexploited pockets of food become sparser and harder to find and the bird community responds by joining into flocks to search together—a single such flock along a hedgerow may contain chaffinches, yellow-hammers, greenfinches, linnets and goldfinches, all of them the more visible for the absence of leaf cover to hide them from view.

CHECKLIST

This checklist is a guide to the birds you will find in fields and hedgerows. Although you will not see them all in the same place, you should be able to spot many of them as you walk through the countryside during the changing seasons. The species listed in **bold** *type are described in detail.*

Blackbird
Blackcap
Bullfinch
Carrion crow
Chaffinch
Cirl bunting
Corn bunting
Cuckoo
Dunnock
Fieldfare
Garden warbler
Goldfinch
Great tit
Greenfinch
Green woodpecker
Jackdaw
Kestrel
Linnet

Little owl
Long-tailed tit
Magpie
Mistle thrush
Partridge
Pheasant
Redwing
Rook
Skylark
Song thrush
Sparrowhawk
Starling
Tree sparrow
Turtle dove
Whitethroat
Woodlark
Wren
Yellowhammer

Above: Kestrel pair in flight. The male is on the right.

Left: The whitethroat, a small, active warbler, frequents hedgerows, undergrowth and woodland edges.

THE KESTREL: HOVERING HUNTER

The kestrel's old folk name – the windhover – catches the essence of this bird whose most characteristic posture is its skilful, seemingly effortless hovering. If you see a bird with wings winnowing, tail fanned out and head down it's probably a kestrel after prey.

A pair of kestrels at their woodland nest; as with many birds of prey, the male (left) is smaller than the female (right). The nest was not built by this pair; it is an old one made by another bird (possibly a carrion crow) and taken over by the kestrels. When the eggs – up to five in number – are laid, the female does most of the incubating while the male hunts, periodically bringing his mate food – such as the vole she is holding in her beak.

The kestrel is our most common and widespread bird of prey; it is also unique in the way it has come to terms with man and become an independent and resourceful city dweller. Its urban takeover bid has been very successful; in a special survey carried out in 1977 no fewer than 337 breeding pairs were reported in London, at least seven of them right in the heart of the city. The kestrel has also learned to exploit the thousands of miles of infrequently mown grassy motorway verges which harbour the small rodents that make up its principal food. In fact, a stretch of country motorway is one of the best places to see these slim, long-tailed members of the falcon family. Male and female do not look alike. The striking blue-grey head and tail ar light chestnut back spotted with black identi the male kestrel, while the female's pluma, is barred and streaked in brown and reddis brown colours. Both sexes have a co spicuous black band on the end of the t which is clearly visible when the birds a hovering, and both have creamy underpar streaked with black or dark brown.

Varied feeder Towns and motorways a not, of course, the only haunts of the kestre It frequents downs, heaths, moors, mou tains, parkland, farmland and cliffs – almo every land habitat barring the middle of thic woods where there is not enough room for i particular style of hunting. (In these woo

The kestrel's hunting technique

Left: The hunting kestrel holds its position in the air with continuous small corrective movements of outstretched wings and tail while at the same time keeping its down-pointed head (and eyes) perfectly steady.

kestrel's place is taken by the sparrow-
wk).

One secret of the kestrel's success is its
ility to adapt to a very varied diet. In
untry areas small rodents such as mice and
les form nearly two thirds of the kestrel's
od–making the bird a distinct benefit to
 farmer. The next most important items of
t are insects, particularly grasshoppers and
etles, and some small birds such as finches.
me enterprising individuals have been
own to take turtle doves and lapwings–
ds almost as large as themselves.

In towns where small outdoor mammals are
short supply, the kestrel preys principally
 small birds such as house sparrows and
rlings. Distance is no serious obstacle if
 kestrel knows that a good supply of food
aits it at the end of a journey; for instance,
e pair of outer London kestrels flew five
les regularly to hunt at a sewage works
quented by starlings.

Skilled hunter The kestrel is an exception-
y keen sighted bird–as it has to be since it
ten hunts from heights of up to 60m (200ft).
 it hovers, the kestrel keeps its head
solutely still–eyes fixed on the prey far
low–while maintaining its position in the
 with constant small adjustments of wings

Right: To catch its prey the kestrel must be fast and accurate. When its keen eyes have picked out the movements of a mouse or vole on the ground below, the kestrel swoops down on it in a series of stepped descents. The kill is made with the strong, fearsomely sharp talons which clutch the victim in a deadly grip. Open ground is essential for this type of hunting–in dense woodland with tangled undergrowth the kestrel could severely damage its long, pointed wings.

Below: After the kill, the kestrel sometimes 'mantles' its prey, with its wings outspread and its tail forming an almost circular cover. It is thought this is done to screen the prey while the bird recovers from the flurry of the hunt.

watchful hover

normal roving flight

swoop down to lower level

final hover before dropping on prey

Left: Although the kestrel will sometimes eat its prey on the ground, it prefers to carry it to a secluded perch. The feet grip the prey firmly while the strong hooked beak tears off flesh.

and tail. Even when facing into a high wind, the head remains quite steady though the body may be wobbling frantically from side to side and the wings and tail lashing furiously.

Once the victim is spotted, the kestrel swoops towards it at great speed, sometimes catching up short halfway to adjust position, and seizes the unfortunate animal with its powerful outstretched talons. The prey either dies instantly from the impact, or when a talon pierces a vital organ during a tussle on the ground. If the kill is made on a roadside verge or other exposed place, the kestrel flies off at once to a private perch, clutching its prey firmly in its talons. Alternatively, the kestrel will crouch over its kill on the ground, 'mantling' it with outspread wings and tail – like an open umbrella. It is thought that this is done to screen the prey from other birds while giving the kestrel time to regain its breath after the exertion of the hunt; it is an aspect of behaviour typical of all falcons. Small birds are sometimes caught on the wing in a swift 'swoop, clutch and away' movement. The prey is usually carried off to a suitable perch or post, where the kestrel can eat it in peace and quiet. Fence posts, telephone wires and tall trees are often used as convenient perches from which the kestrel can watch for prey; its alert, straight-backed posture on these perches is almost as characteristic a pose as the hovering. The swoop down on a victim is made just as effectively from this position.

Choosing a nesting site Like other falcons, the kestrel does not build a nest. In the country it often lays its eggs on cliff ledges, in hollow trees or, in wooded areas, in the old nest of another bird – particularly that of the carrion crow. On the Orkney Islands which have a good supply of food to offer but neither cliffs nor trees, the kestrel has learned to nest in long heather on the ground.

In towns, however, the kestrel's adaptability is especially evident in its catholic choice of nesting site. Ruined and deserted buildings have long been used as substitutes for cliffs and from these it seems to have been a simple stage to nesting on occupied buildings. Most early town-breeding records refer to public buildings like churches. One famous pair of kestrels managed to raise their family on the tower of the Imperial Institute in South Kensington! More recently, kestrels have been discovered breeding in window boxes on high-rise buildings – perhaps the ultimate in city acclimatisation.

Kestrels are great opportunists; in the Netherlands, for example, they were quick to benefit from the invasion of rodents on the newly reclaimed Zuider Zee polders, and readily occupied the large open-fronted nest boxes put up for them by the thoughtful Dutch.

Courtship display Kestrels are rather solitary birds, so it is only during courtship that you are likely to see male and female together.

The pair soar up into the sky with extended wings, the male usually higher than his mate. Soaring is followed by much wilder movements – the male repeatedly 'stoops' upon the female like a fighter plane in aerial combat, sometimes even brushing her with his wings. This dramatic display is often accompanied by loud, rather shrill 'kee-kee-kee' calls.

The soaring display flight is perhaps the only time when you might confuse the kestrel with our other small bird of prey, the sparrowhawk. Both birds are similar enough in size to cause confusion, both have a long tail and both soar in the breeding season. However, if you watch for the sparrowhawk's distinctive low-level interception method of killing (as opposed to the kestrel's characteristic hover), and broad, blunt wings (unlike the kestrel's long pointed ones) identification should not be too difficult. Sometimes, however, the kestrel's wings can look broad and blunt-ended when they are stiffly extended during soaring.

Raising young The female kestrel lays her eggs between mid-April and mid-May, at intervals of two to four days. The eggs, from one to five in number, are a rich, mottled red brown in colour.

The female incubates the eggs for about a month, sometimes assisted by the male. Occasionally, she will start incubating as soon as the first egg is laid (instead of when all are laid, as is more usual), so the young may hatch

out at two- to four-day intervals. This is an adaptation for species survival, for in years when food is scarce the smallest and weakest (and probably the youngest) quickly starve to death; in this case it is better to raise just one healthy, strong chick rather than four or more weaklings.

Both male and female take part in feeding the chicks; these develop not one but two successive coats of greyish fluffy down before fledging at about 28-30 days old. The young are meat eaters from the start of their lives and greedily swallow the chunks of flesh and insects offered them by their parents until they are old enough to leave the nest and hunt for themselves.

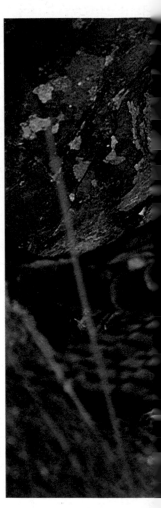

Above: Female kestrel and her brood on a rocky cliff ledge nesting site. Both male and female feed the chicks, bringing voles, mice and insects.

Left: The kestrel chick has two successive coats of down, the first shorter and thinner and the second longer, coarser and usually darker. Feathers start to appear when the chick is between 12 and 20 days old, and the chick is able to fly at anything from 27 to 39 days.

Kestrel (Falco tinnunculus), also called the windhover; 34cm (13½in) long from beak to tail; distribution very general, including open woods, moors, cliffs, farmland, motorway verges and city centres.

How birds see

Vision is the dominant sense of nearly all birds. In most, the eyes are placed so far to the side of the head that they have mainly monocular vision—each eye scanning a separate area—a feature shared by all hunted creatures who depend on vision to warn them of possible danger. The thrush turns its head sideways to look (not to listen), and some birds, such as the woodcock, even have all round vision. Birds of prey and owls have eyes set more to the front of the head, offering a wider angle of binocular vision—vitally important for judging distance. The kestrel, for example, has a 150° field of vision, over the middle 50° of which both eyes work in binocular vision, scanning an overlapping area.

We see only the cornea of a bird's eye, but the eyeball within the skull is proportionately huge. For example, if our eyes were like the starling's, they would be as big as tennis balls! A bird focuses by means of powerful muscles which alter the shape of the lens. Light passing through the lens falls on the retina—a complex surface of minute cells. Part of the retina— the fovea—is more densely packed with cells: in the buzzard there are one million per square millimetre, while in man there are only 200,000. The more cells there are, the greater the detail transmitted to the brain. (Some of the cells are responsive to light, while others respond to colour.) Elsewhere within the bird's eye is a small, fleshy projection called the pecten, which supplies oxygen and nutrients to the cells and also enhances the ability of the eye to detect movement. Many birds have oil droplets within their eyes which serve to sharpen contrast (as a photographic filter does), making it easier for the bird to distinguish its prey. Also birds have a third 'eyelid'—a transparent nictitating (winking) membrane—which moves sideways across the cornea and keeps it moist without interrupting vision. This makes birds look as though they blink.

Accuracy is crucial for a hunting bird like the kestrel which relies on its keen eyesight, first to spot prey and then to catch it; the kestrel's eyes are therefore positioned sufficiently far forwards to give it binocular (three-dimensional) vision over a third of its visual arc.

THIEVING MAGPIES

The magpie is notorious for its habit of stealing other birds' eggs and chicks. You are most likely to catch it in the act in summer—at other times it eats almost anything.

Magpies are members of the crow family and are easily distinguished from their relatives—indeed from all other British birds—by their distinctive black and white colouring. Whether young or old, male or female, all have the same boldly patterned plumage which, at a distance, is only black and white, without any other colours.

Nest predators Like others of the crow family, magpies will often plunder eggs and nestlings of less aggressive neighbours—particularly in farmland. Searching methodically for a suitable nest-worthy habitat, such as a thick, overgrown hedge, a single magpie may find several nests in quick succession. When a small bird sitting on a nest sees a magpie, it may 'freeze' until the last possible moment—hoping to be missed. Once the magpie

Above: You cannot miss a magpie—its black and white plumage is striking and unlike that of any other bird in the British Isles.
Magpie (*Pica pica*), 45cm (18in) from beak to tip of tail. Resident. Distribution—see map below.

Magpie distribution

Magpies are probably capable of living anywhere in the British Isles, but the present breeding distribution is distinctly patchy in northern England and Scotland. Here persecution from gamekeepers—who rear grouse on the moors and pheasants in the valleys and dislike the magpie's habit of stealing eggs—is still common. Built-up areas with less keepering around cities such as Glasgow and Aberdeen act as refuges and support expanding populations. Gaps in eastern England may reflect changing agricultural practices.

covers it however, the other bird must
reat hastily, and magpies have even been
en catching small birds in flight.

Like birds of prey, magpies are mobbed by
aller birds that must have no difficulty in
cognising this particular enemy. Large
ds are generally better off against magpies;
eir nests are only robbed when left un-
arded, so the parents sit tight regardless.

When there is plenty of food, the nest of a
d such as the woodpigeon (in which both
xes incubate the eggs) is only uncovered
ring the changeovers, so the magpie may
ake several visits before it gets a meal. In
me other species where only the female
rd incubates the eggs, she must feed and
turn to the nest as soon as possible,
pecially if the eggs are not well hidden from
w. In only a few seconds a magpie can
rce its way to a nest and eat or carry off the
gs or nestlings–leaving only a few frag-
ents of eggshell. The magpie's job is
latively easy early in the summer when
esting cover is thin and food shortage forces
any birds to spend more time feeding and
ss time incubating. Fortunately most birds
n lay another clutch of eggs.

Wide-ranging diet Apart from this form of
undering–which is really a summer side-
ne–magpies mainly eat insects and larvae
ich as ground-dwelling beetles and moth
aterpillars. However, magpies are opportu-
sts and take whatever food they find. They
at small mammals such as voles and mice
nd also carrion. Magpies also feed on the
ore nutritious parts of plant matter such as
uits, nuts, berries and cereal grains, as
ell as on some invertebrates–slugs, snails
nd worms–and a range of household scraps.
ccasionally you may see magpies perching
n the backs of farm animals where they
at fly larvae and parasitic ticks, as well as

matt
velvety head

white
shoulder patch
and underparts

iridescent
wing feathers

long wedge-shaped
iridescent tail

white
inner webs on
flight feathers

Above: The magpie's flight
is usually direct and several
magpies may follow each
other in single file. The inner
webs of the main flight
feathers are white.
Left: At close range,
especially in bright sunlight,
iridescent green and purple
colours are reflected by the
magpie's wing and tail
feathers.

pluck hair or wool to line their nests.

Nests and young The best time to look for
magpie nests is in the winter, when the trees
have no leaves. Each spring magpies have a
strong tendency to return to their old nests–
adding to them or building on top of them.
The nests may be renovated but still stay
empty for two months before the female lays
her eggs.

Magpie nest sites range from the top of tall,
isolated trees to thick, thorny hedges or
thickets at the edge of a wood, and even on
sea-cliffs. Though easy to see, the nests are
rarely easy to reach.

The nest is constructed of sticks, and is
thickly lined with mud and a layer of grass
roots. Most magpies also build a dome of
thorny twigs above the nest, leaving only a
single, inconspicuous entrance at the side.
The parents, which are said to pair for life,
participate in building.

The female lays her eggs in April and has
only one brood per year. The number of
eggs varies from five to eight, though up to
ten have been recorded. Only the female
incubates the eggs, which take about 17 days
to hatch. After this both parents feed the
nestlings for three to four weeks. You can see
family parties of magpies throughout the
late summer and autumn; and you may spy
the young jumping around using their short
tails to help them balance each time they land.

Decline and rise Magpies are more widely
distributed in the world than any other crow
except the raven. In the British Isles, however,
their distribution has been affected by many
years of persecution. Shooting, poisoned
bait and traps have reduced the magpie
population throughout Scotland and parts of
England. In some game-rearing areas it was
eliminated altogether. Though many are still

Below: Magpies find much
of their food on the ground,
such as this dead rabbit.
They walk or hop along the
surface with the tail held a
little elevated.

shot and hung from the gamekeeper's gibbet, a substantial recovery has been recorded this century. The introduction of laws prohibiting the use of poison and traps, and a decrease in game rearing has encouraged increases in the magpie's numbers and range, particularly during the last 40 years.

Moreover, magpies show an ability to survive changing conditions in a variety of habitats. They have colonised built-up areas as well as open country–a trend that is still continuing. In Scotland, where there are still large gaps in their distribution, the magpie has strongholds around cities such as Aberdeen, Glasgow and Edinburgh. In Ireland, magpies now breed in every county– as they do in England and Wales. Recently the only noticeable declines have been in country areas of England, particularly in East Anglia where the grubbing up of woodland and hedgerows and use of pesticides are thought to be the cause.

Distribution The spread of the magpies' distribution from the natural habitat of woodland edge, grassland and farmland to the man-made habitat of towns and cities reflects the species' adaptability. From the parks and large gardens of suburban London, they have spread in the last ten years to such places as Hyde Park and Buckingham Palace Gardens. Magpies are not fussy about their choice of food, habitat or company, and seem well fitted to life with man–if man allows it.

Bold and inquisitive It is worth watching magpies closely. They are constantly inquisitive and are known to hoard bright objects. Often they seem 'visibly intelligent' –soaking dry bread in a fishpond, for example, to make it easier to eat; then hiding the excess in a crevice in the rockery, carefully covering it with moss and grass pulled from the lawn.

Frequent raucous chattering makes magpies within earshot difficult to miss, and they often strut about in open grassy fields, or perch conspicuously on the top of fences and trees. It appears that their robust and intelligent nature, coupled with a large, sharp beak, is sufficient to deter most natural predators, so that secrecy and camouflage are of limited value.

Magpies are always alert, and city birds are quick to give warning of approaching cats, and they are becoming increasingly bold and some regularly visit bird tables. Of course they are not always welcome, especially as they thieve from the nests of garden birds. Magpies have even been seen drinking milk from the bottle like tits, and in Manchester they now take advantage of the eggs left in the cartons alongside the milk.

Telling the future Magpies have an important place in British folklore. Most people know of the good or bad luck that is supposed to follow if one or more magpies crosses their path. Your fortune or fate depends on the number you see, what the magpies are doing and where in the country you are.

Are birds 'intelligent'–or do they just imitate?

Magpies and other members of the crow family are often classed as the most intelligent of all birds. They are able to learn complex behaviour patterns and can be taught to 'talk' and count up to three or four. They survive heavy persecution and adapt to changing environments. Tits are also placed high on the intelligence scale–they are good at finding peanuts, and experiments have shown that they can be taught to obtain food from trick peanut-holders. The rapid spread of the habit of opening milk bottle tops clearly illustrates that they can both imitate others and discover for themselves. However, it is difficult to equate our anthropomorphic view of intelligence with the natural 'intelligence' of all birds.

Magpies are naturally inquisitive, and can handle a variety of foods in the countryside, so observations of 'intelligent' behaviour in built-up areas are not surprising. Similarly, the ability of tits to find and use man-made food is an extension of their natural feeding techniques. They need to be skilful at finding food in their natural woodland habitat; so they explore every possible nook and cranny, tearing and chipping bark away from holes where insects might hide. As they move into the suburban environment, these birds will find peanuts and milk, and treat them in the same way as normal foods.

Perhaps the 'intelligence' test should be related to birds' innate ability to build nests, migrate or even feed. How many people could build even an ordinary nest like that of a blackbird, or navigate like the migrating swallow, or collect 10,000 caterpillars in 18 days to feed a brood of blue tits?

Right: The female lays five to eight eggs in a nest that can be up to one metre (3ft) in diameter. The eggs, which are pale green with grey and brown spots or blotches, are about 3.5cm (1¼in) long. Since there are only four eggs here, the clutch has probably not yet been completed.

Below: The young magpies leave the nest in June or July, and are distinguished by their stubby, incomplete tails.

ROOKS: NOISY COMMUNAL NESTERS

If any one species of bird typifies the British countryside, it is surely the rook. But sadly the rook, or 'church parson' as it is known in some parts of the country, has been steadily declining in numbers for some years and no one yet knows why.

ook (*Corvus frugilegus*). ember of the crow family— d the most sociable. und as resident roughout the British Isles, ough scarce in the lands of Scotland and ales and the Scottish lands. Length 46cm (18in).

The rook is an integral part of our countryside and has become the subject of a considerable amount of folklore—though much of it is misleading. For example, the height at which it nests is said to be a sure guide to the weather that spring, high nests signifying fine weather and low nests bad weather. In fact, rooks tend to occupy the same nests each year. Another myth surrounding rooks is that they hold 'parliaments' in which social justice is supposed to be meted out to their peers.

One piece of folklore about rooks is, however, partly true. This is the adage 'One for the rook, one for the crow, one to rot and one to grow', which describes the fate of corn after sowing. Newly sown seed is an important part of the rooks' diet and great damage can be caused to crops. But the adage is wrong to suggest that crows are equally destructive. Most damage is caused by rooks and their distinctly smaller cousins, the jackdaws. Crows are blamed only because they look so similar to rooks.

Rooks and crows Distinguishing rooks from crows takes a little practice. Rooks are generally slightly smaller (about 45cm/18in long) than crows (47cm/19in long); their coats are glossy blue when seen at close range, whereas crows have a duller plumage. More distinctive are the white patch of bare skin around the adult rooks' bill and the long feathers around the upper part of the legs which resemble baggy trousers. Crows have

glossy plumage

white face-patch

thigh feathers

Rook

rounded tail

lacks face-patch

juvenile rook

Crow

duller plumage

lacks thigh feathers

Adult rooks have a distinctive white patch at the base of their beaks, and feathered legs that help to distinguish them from crows. Juvenile rooks are more easily confused since they lack the face patch, but their 'baggy trousers' and smaller size help distinguish them from crows.

neither of these features.

The juvenile rook is much more easily confused with a crow since its plumage is duller and it lacks the white patch at the base of its bill. But the young rook still has the 'baggy trousers' and its smaller size helps to distinguish it. In flight, rooks can be distinguished by their rounded tail.

Another adage, 'One rook is a crow and a flock of crows are rooks', attempts to distinguish the two species by their social behaviour. Unfortunately, this is not a reliable guide since rooks, especially juveniles, sometimes feed on their own and crows can form large flocks.

Courtship rituals Although the rook's breeding season begins around March and April, courtship–an elaborate affair–occurs from autumn onwards. The courtship display involves the male energetically bowing with tail fanned in front of his existing or prospective mate. The female sometimes bows in return; more often she crouches, wings quivering, in a posture closely resembling that of a nestling begging for food–which is exactly what she is doing, for feeding forms an important part of the courtship display. The male and female usually pair for life, but each year the bond between two birds is strengthened through displays.

Communal nesting Rooks nest communally in rookeries. These may contain as many as 3000 nests but most have less than 50,

particularly in England. In Scotland, roo[keries] eries tend to be larger.

A rookery is inhabited by breeding adul[ts] but it also contains birds in their first ye[ar] trying to obtain mates and nest-sites–so[me] even trying to breed. At one time, rooker[ies] were particularly common in churchyar[ds] hence the country name of the rook–'chur[ch] parson'.

Both members of the pair help to build t[he] nest. The main building material is tw[igs] broken off from trees, taken from the grou[nd] or even stolen from nearby nests. Parts [of] the nest may be cemented with mud and the[re] is usually a lining of leaves, grass and oth[er] suitable material.

Eggs, young and branchers In sprin[g] between three and five eggs are laid at da[ily] intervals. The eggs are greenish or blue wi[th] dense grey or brown markings. They a[re] incubated for 16-18 days by just the fema[le] during which time the male feeds the fema[le].

When the young hatch the mother broo[ds] them continually, while the male feeds t[he] whole family. Once the chicks are about t[en] days old the female joins her mate in feedi[ng] them and also flies off by herself to feed.

The young leave the nest when they a[re] about 30 days old. At this stage they a[re] unable to fly and spend a few days climbi[ng] around nearby nests, when they are know[n] as 'branchers'. In rural areas branchers a[re] often killed in organised shoots held eac[h]

Above: A female rook (centre) begging for food from her mate (top right) as part of the courtship ritual. Here you can see that the pouch of bare skin at the base of the male's bill is bulging with stored food.

Right: A rook's nest consists mostly of twigs lined with moss, feathers, grasses and leaves. The eggs are greenish or blue with dark markings.

...ht: Rooks typically ...ed in open country, ...ablishing their nests ...mmunally, high up in ...s. These are the familiar ...keries that can be seen so ...arly in winter when many ...s are bare.

...low right: Rooks probing ... soil invertebrates such as ...thworms and larvae, ...ich form a major part of ...ir diet. In feeding on ...m, rooks help both the ...mer and the gardener ...ce many of these ...ertebrates are pests. ...t rooks themselves are ...arded as pests since they ...o feed off cereal grain.

...ay. Until the end of the last war they were ...ken to London and sold in the markets. ...oday, these shoots are still held in some ...eas–ostensibly to control the numbers of ...oks (though to little effect), but also as a ...ditional part of country life.

When the young reach about three or four ...eeks old, they leave the rookery but remain ...pendent on the parents for food for another ...onth. At this time, they noisily follow the ...ults in the fields and vigorously beg with ...ivering wings whenever one of them finds ...od.

Food supply Rooks feed predominantly on ... diet of soil invertebrates, such as earth-...orms and leatherjackets, and cereal grain, ...ough the young receive a diet consisting ...ainly of invertebrates. Winter is a time of ...enty for the rook since there are large ...mbers of soil invertebrates available and ...inter-sown cereals provide an abundant ...ource of grain.

In contrast, summer is often a difficult ...me for rooks. Grain is absent, since the ...ummer crop will not yet have ripened, and ...vertebrates are often hard to come by, since ...any earthworms either become inactive or ...urrow deep into the soil beyond the bird's ...ach and leatherjackets have metamor-...hosed into adult craneflies. In southern ...ngland, rooks may be able to find some ...sect food in the form of caterpillars but, in ...neral, invertebrate food is scarce in the ...ummer.

To make matters worse, rooks undergo ...heir annual moult in the summer and they ...eed a plentiful supply of food if they are to ...row a new set of feathers. It is not surprising ...hat peak mortality occurs at this time of ...ear, mainly through starvation. Yet, over ...he year, rooks fare no worse than many other ...irds since they survive so much better than

most during the winter.

Declining numbers This century has seen Britain's rook population decline steadily; numbers have fallen by half in the last 30 years. Yet the annual summer drop in numbers has no lasting effect, nor are control efforts by farmers responsible–at least 50% of branchers shot in the spring would die from starvation the following summer, anyway. A possible factor, and one often quoted, is that Dutch elm disease has helped to reduce the rook population by destroying sites for rookeries. But this seems unlikely. In areas where this disease has been particularly severe, the rooks have simply moved into other trees for nesting.

Rook populations have been declining in many other parts of Europe, apart from Britain, and it is now thought to be due to widespread agricultural or climatic changes. But more research is going on to find out the exact causes.

So far, there is no sign that the rate of decline of the 'church parson' is even slowing down, but it must be hoped that it will soon.

Winter survival

It may seem strange that winter rather than summer is the season of plenty for rooks. Yet the same situation holds for other species of birds, such as starlings and jackdaws, which have a similar diet to that of rooks. For all these species the high survival rate during winter is a fairly recent phenomenon created by farmers providing an abundant source of winter food in the form of seed. Other omnivorous feeders, such as song thrushes, that are less able to take advantage of man's activities can suffer badly in bad winters. The winter of 1962-3 killed many of these birds.

THE LITTLE OWL: TWILIGHT HUNTER

Owls are usually regarded as birds of the night, but not all of them fit into this stereotype. The little owl is active during the day and can often be seen perching in some prominent place, although it does most of its hunting at dawn and dusk.

Little owl (*Athene noctua*). Resident bird of prey; at 23cm (9in) long, the smallest British owl. Its habitat ranges from open farmland and wasteland to urban areas, but it avoids woodland.

Owls are well known for their extraordinarily keen eyesight that enables them to hunt at night. Yet they can see just as well during the day, though few owls take advantage of this to hunt while the light is still good. The reason for this is that their victims – mice, voles, worms and insects – are mostly nocturn-al creatures.

A few species of owl, however, prefer to b active throughout the day. One of these is th little owl, which does most of its hunting a dawn and dusk. In this way, it can hunt bot daytime and nocturnal creatures.

Where to see little owls The ideal habitat fc little owls is open farmland with old trees an buildings to provide nesting sites. Othe favourite haunts include old orchard: quarries and wasteground, and it is not ur usual to find them near the coast among san dunes or around cliffs and islands. Some hav even adapted to an urban environment an nest in city centres. The only habitat they seer to avoid is woodland, probably because thi is the domain of the much larger tawny ow which is known to eat little owls.

The best way to see a little owl is to sca its favourite perching places: telegraph pole; fence posts, stone walls, the roofs of building and prominent rocks and branches of tree Seen from a distance the little owl is easil overlooked because its greyish colour an

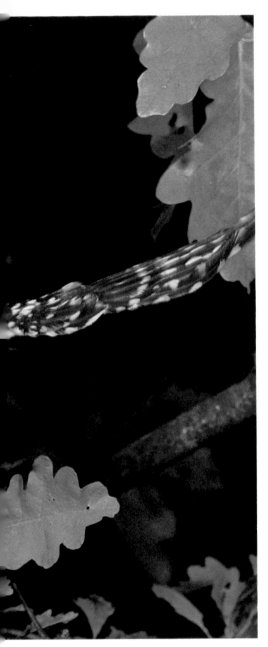

bright yellow
eyes with
dark pupils

heavily barred
underwings

Little owl

Tawny owl 38cm (15in)

Right: Little owls can be distinguished from other owls by their much smaller size. For example, they are about half as big as a tawny owl. Both male and female owls have the same plumage and are about the same size as each other.

Below: A little owl perching outside its nest. Its relatively large feet and sharp talons are made for pouncing on prey and killing it.

Little owl 23cm (9in)

quat rounded shape blend well into the background.

The little owl's flight and call are useful aids to identification. Its flight is deeply undulating and resembles that of a woodpecker. The two most distinctive calls are a shrill barking 'werro' and a more plaintive mewing 'kiew', noises that can often be heard when two little owls call to each other. Little owls also make a high-pitched penetrating 'ooo', repeated every few seconds, and they have an alarm call – a loud 'kip-kip-kip' – used by adults to warn their brood of danger.

Distinctive markings At close quarters the little owl is easily identified by its beautiful and distinctive markings. Both the male and the female have grey-brown upperparts with white bars and spots. The underparts are whitish with dark brown streaks. Their eyes are a distinctive bright yellow with large black pupils.

As its name suggests, the little owl is small in comparison with other owls. At 23cm (9in) from head to tail it is by far the smallest

British owl and is about as long as a song thrush. But its large rounded head and broad wings make it look much bigger.

Feet for killing For such a small body the little owl's feet seem abnormally large, but they need to be since the little owl sometimes kills quite large prey. A little owl can pounce on unsuspecting prey with astonishing speed, and the strength of its talons usually kills the prey outright. If it does not then one swift slash from its razor-sharp beak is enough to finish off the victim.

As with all other owls, the little owl has keen eyesight and acute hearing with which to detect its prey–the slightest movement or noise attracts its attention.

Little owls often hunt for food standing still, waiting until they see a potential prey moving and then running to catch it. They also watch for prey from perching sites.

The little owl's diet depends largely on what is available in its vicinity. It includes slugs, snails, centipedes, minnows, frogs and even jackdaws and mistle thrushes, which are both larger than itself. But the usual diet of the little owl consists of small rodents, insects, earthworms and a few small birds.

Prey up to the size of a mouse is swallowed whole but the larger catches are usually taken away to a roosting site such as a hole to be dismembered. As with other owls, the little owl makes no attempt to sort out the digestible parts from the rest of the carcase. This is

Above and below: From three to five white eggs are laid in April or May. The young are white and downy at first, but soon darken as their adult plumage develops.

done in the stomach. Each day the owl coug up a pellet consisting of the indigestible par such as bones, fur, teeth and feathers. The pellets are about 2.5-4cm (1-1½in) long ar can be seen accumulating around the ow daytime roosting sites.

In times when food is plentiful little ow establish secret hiding places where th build up larders of food. As well as providir a store of food for the future they seem prefer their food a little 'high'. And there an additional advantage: the rotting foc attracts flies and beetles, which the owls e as well.

Nesting in holes Little owls nest in hole usually in old trees, in which case they a likely to choose a hole that has two exits. The may also nest in a cavity in a stone wall c an old building, or in a disused rabbit warrer Like other owls they do not add material t their nest, though they may nest in a ho that has already been lined, for example a old jackdaw's nest.

In April or May the female lays her egg The typical clutch is three to five eggs, whic are white and elliptical rather than the mo usual egg shape. The female often waits unt the clutch is complete before she begins t incubate it. Incubation is performed by th female alone and takes between three an four weeks. During this time she is fed by th male. Once the eggs hatch both parents hel to feed the young. At first the young owlet are covered with short white down that make them look rather like fluffy tennis balls wit feet. They grow their adult plumage stil in the nest and are ready to leave when the are about five weeks old. Sometimes th parents will then raise a second brood, bu

How the little owl has spread

The first successful attempt to introduce the little owl into Britain was carried out with a set of birds released in Northamptonshire in 1888. These birds bred and multiplied, and others were released elsewhere, so that by 1920 the little owl had spread throughout the Midlands and southern England (except Cornwall) and into Wales. Today it can also be seen in Scotland and Cornwall.

☐ present day distribution

☐ distribution by 1920

● introduction in 1888

ily when food is plentiful.

Young little owls are not abandoned by their parents straight away. They have a month or two to learn where and when to look for food, what to eat and how to catch it. But after that the young are on their own. Many experienced young owls die in hard winters when food is scarce. For example, the British population fell dramatically during the harsh winter of 1962-3. However, their numbers always recover quickly.

Imported from Holland Fossil records show that little owls existed in prehistoric Britain but then became extinct. Our present population is descended from birds brought over from Holland during the last century. In 1888, a flock of little owls released in Northamptonshire bred successfully. Once they were established their population grew rapidly since, in open habitats, they have no competitors. By 1930 little owls were breeding in every county south of the River Humber.

Since then they have continued to spread, but at a slower rate. Some little owls now breed in Scotland, but in general the climate there is too harsh for them, and it seems that the Irish Sea is too wide for them to fly over and invade Ireland. There has even been a decrease in their numbers in southern England, possibly because of the presence of pesticides in their prey.

Friend or foe? Little owls were popular when they were first introduced to Britain, but public opinion turned against them in the early part of this century as people began to claim that they killed chickens and game-bird chicks. Many little owls were shot, but in 1935 the British Trust for Ornithology, worried at the number of little owls that were dying, carried out an enquiry. It examined the stomach contents of dead owls, the remains of prey found at nest sites, and thousands of pellets. It soon became clear that, although little owls do occasionally eat game-bird chicks, most of their diet consists of animals that are themselves pests. So, instead of being the pests that people thought them to be, little owls are actually beneficial to man by helping him to control his natural enemies.

Right: Three young little owls at their nest hole. When nervous both young and adult little owls bob their heads up and down in a characteristically comical manner.

Below: The young are fed largely on a diet of insects and earthworms. Both parents help to catch the food and feed the young. At about five weeks old, the young owls leave the nest, but they remain dependent on the parents until they learn to hunt.

Reed bunting

black hood

Yellowhammer (*Emberiz citrina*); resident farmland bird, with yellow plumage, especially on head of male 17cm (6½in).

Left: A male yellowhamme sits on a typical songpost. You can often hear the yellowhammer's jingling territorial song from late February to August or even September. Traditionally this familiar sound is verbalised as 'a-little-bit-of-bread-and-no-cheese'. A more accurate version migh be 'chi-chi-chi-chi-chi-chi-chi-chi-chee'. At breeding time, his song warns other males where his territory is.

HANDSOME BUNTINGS

Two of our smartest buntings are the yellowhammer and the cirl bunting. The yellowhammer is well suited to our climate, but the cirl bunting is really a Mediterranean species.

Buntings are slender songbirds that look similar to finches, with the same stocky seed-eating bills. However, they generally prefer more open country, feed mainly on the ground and have less musical or varied songs than finches. In all except the corn bunting, the male is brightly coloured – male yellowhammers and cirl buntings are particularly attractive – but females and young birds are drab and inconspicuous.

Vivid yellow The male yellowhammer is yellower than all other British birds except the yellow wagtail, and in summer his head is almost totally bright lemon yellow. His underside is also yellow, but with a brownish breast-band and a few brown streaks on the flanks. His upperparts are chestnut, and attractively marked with black and brown except for the rump, which is plain. The outer tail feathers are mostly white.

All yellowhammers, whatever their age or sex, have a chestnut-coloured rump – an important distinguishing mark. Young birds and females are much less yellow than males, particularly on the head. They are more heavily streaked and, apart from the rump, are easily confused with cirl buntings.

Active farmland life Yellowhammers are familiar farmland birds; in winter you find them feeding on stubble fields and ploughed land, mingling freely with larks and finches. Often the male's yellow head is the first thing

Below: Yellowhammers make their nests out of gras and a little moss, and line them with hair, fine grass and roots. Most choose a site within a couple of feet of the ground. Many actually nest on the ground hidden among grass and other low plants. Some lay eggs as early as mid-April, but most start in May. The eggs are whitish or pinkish, with fine, irregular dark brown squiggles and a blotch or two.

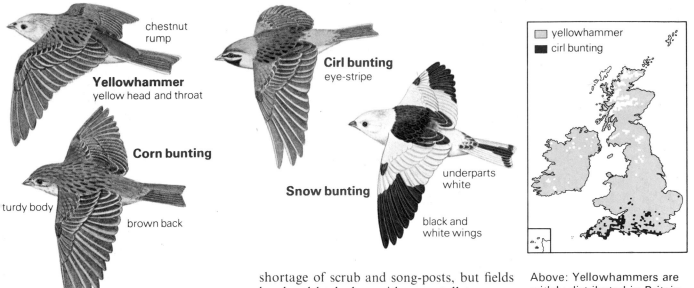

chestnut
rump

Yellowhammer
yellow head and throat

Corn bunting

turdy body

brown back

Cirl bunting
eye-stripe

Snow bunting

underparts
white

black and
white wings

yellowhammer
cirl bunting

see as he hops along in a low, crouched
sition. They often flock together at feeding
ces, and if disturbed fly into nearby trees
safety. In flight, yellowhammers have
ticeably long, white-edged tails and a
ghtly bounding action. Often they call as
y pass over – a sharp 'chip' or 'chillip'.
other characteristic call is a low 'dzee'.
They eat mainly seeds, especially leftover
n and the seeds of grass and weeds. They
o eat wild fruits such as blackberries and,
summer, insect larvae, beetles, spiders,
llipedes, and even slugs and earthworms.
Mixed habitat Yellowhammers nest in
most any country area. Ideally they need
en ground for feeding, low scrub for
sting and taller bushes or trees as song-
sts. Their favourite habitat is the edge of
young conifer plantation where brambles
d other plants are still common; here they
ch densities of up to 58 pairs in a square
ometre (150 per square mile). Most of our
mland has an excess of open ground and a

shortage of scrub and song-posts, but fields
bordered by hedges with some tall trees are
nevertheless quite suitable. Heaths and commons with clumps of hawthorn bushes have
always been good yellowhammer sites, but in
recent years the birds have spread into woodland.

During the cold winter of 1962-63, the
whole yellowhammer population was severely
reduced, but since then it has recovered well
and there are signs that it was relatively un-
harmed by the cold snap in January 1982.
Each year, the best breeding sites are occupied very early in spring, and late arrivals
occupy whatever sites they can. However,
now that the population is large again, farmland has become overcrowded, leading to an
overspill into woodland rides and edges.
Normally yellowhammers ignore these far-
from-ideal sites, but since the only alternative
is a tiny patch of farmland already filled to
capacity, they have little choice.

Bird of many names In the past, the yellowhammer has been known by over 20 different
names. Its bright plumage is mentioned in
many of these. In Scotland, its local names

Above: Yellowhammers are
widely distributed in Britain
and Ireland, while cirl
buntings are limited to
southern England. Most
birds of both species rarely
travel more than a few miles
in their lifetime.

Above: left: There are five
buntings that nest in
Britain and Ireland, the
most common and colourful
being the yellowhammer.
The cirl (pronounced serl)
bunting has a very similar
plumage but is quite rare.
Two of the other species
are common: the corn
bunting – most frequent
around cornfields – and the
reed bunting, which favours
wetlands. The snow bunting
is a very rare British
breeder; only a handful of
pairs nest on mountains in
Scotland, though many more
visit us in winter.

ght: A female
lowhammer at her nest.
e usual clutch is three or
r eggs, but clutches tend
be smaller in conditions
overcrowding, in poor
bitats, in northerly areas
very early or late in the
eding season; this is
ely to be because there is
t sufficient food for the
rents to cope with large
ods in these
cumstances. As laying can
ntinue until August, each
r has time for three
ccessive broods, but egg-
aling magpies limit some
only two. Incubation
es 12-14 days and is
gely the responsibility
the female, who is far
ter camouflaged than the
le. The young fly at 12-
days.

Above: The easiest way to find a cirl bunting is to listen for the male's rather simple, monotonous song. It sounds like a hurried yellowhammer's song (without the 'cheese'), but it can be hard to judge because yellowhammers themselves sometimes do not complete their song. The song is also often compared to the final rattle of the song of the lesser whitethroat—a warbler which sometimes nests close by. The cirl bunting's usual call is a weak, squeaky 'seep'.

Cirl bunting (*Emberiza cirlus*); resident in farmland in southern England; not unlike the yellowhammer but with black chin and eye-stripe, and olive colour on rump. 17cm (6½in).

include yellow bunting, yellow yorling, yellow yite and yellow yoit; and in some English counties it is known as the yellow amber, yellow yowlie and yellow ring. The lines on its eggs give rise to names such as writing master, scribbling or writing lark, scribblie and scribbler.

Cirl buntings These birds are stockier and slightly shorter-tailed than yellowhammers, but have very similar habits. Their food seems to be similar and you may see both species feeding together. Pairs are usually widely scattered, so that although family groups stay together in autumn and winter, they do not form large flocks.

An adult male cirl bunting is a handsome bird with very distinctive head pattern (although, as with the yellowhammer, breeding colours are subdued in winter). He has a black chin, a yellow-bordered black eye-stripe and a greyish streaked crown. Across the breast is a greyish-green band, and the flanks are chestnut coloured. The rest of the underparts, the tail and the back are similar to those of the yellowhammer except

for the rump, which is an inconspicuous o colour and not chestnut.

As with yellowhammers, female and yo cirl buntings are less distinctive, browner more heavily streaked, but they still have tell-tale olive-coloured rump. They lack male's head markings, although the fem has faint yellow stripes above and below eye.

The song period, breeding season choice of nest site are similar to those of yellowhammer. Sometimes the cirl bunt nests in a large garden on the edge of a villa in which case the male may sing from a r top or television aerial. The female b builds the nest and incubates the eggs, bu fed by her mate at this time. Even when is feeding nestlings, he gives the food to and she distributes it.

A more southern species England is c rently the most northerly outpost of the bunting; they were first discovered breed in Devon in 1800. A century later they w common throughout England and Wales, some bred as far north as Cumberland Yorkshire. However, since then their ra has contracted dramatically, and none n nest north of Worcestershire. At their pe cirl buntings were more common than yell hammers, but now you are lucky to find —only 500 pairs are thought to survive h compared with one million pairs of yello hammers.

The cirl bunting is mainly a Mediterran species, living in vineyards and ora groves, and on warm, bushy slopes. In th places they are still common, and yell hammers have to nest in mountain regions to avoid competition. As you mi expect, in England cirl buntings only rem in the south and south-west—areas w relatively warm summers and mild winters

Left: Female cirl bunting at her nest. Cirl buntings choose sheltered farmland habitats with tall hedges and trees, woodland edge parkland and heaths, especially on south-facing slopes on chalk downland and in coastal valleys. The decline of the cirl bunting may be partly due to destruction of habitat, and also to disturbance; but th underlying factor is probably a change in the climate. The bird is a sedentary species and cannot escape bad weathe our cooler, wetter summer and occasional hard winte since the mid-century hav not been to its liking. Outside this country, the cirl bunting is resident in south and west Europe an north-west Africa.

BIRD WITH A BAND OF GOLD

With a broad yellow band stretching across its wings, the goldfinch lives up to its name. Parents and young birds feed in family groups attractively called 'charms'.

is not just the yellowy gold patch along the ings that makes the goldfinch instantly cognisable. The red, white and black striped ead pattern is also unmistakable. The tail nd rest of the wings are black, with delicate hite markings. In spring look for the white ps to each wing feather—by the end of the ummer when the feathers are nearly a year ld they have often worn away. In flight

you can see the goldfinch's whitish rump, similar to that of a bullfinch or brambling. A warm buff-coloured back and flank feathers complete the bird's neat and tidy appearance.

Seed-eaters Thistles are the goldfinch's most important food plant. It eats the seeds from mid-summer through to autumn, and even in winter if they are still available. Often the goldfinch prefers the easy pickings of seed heads that have fallen to the ground, and leaves the seeds that remain on the plants. These then provide a useful reserve of food when snow covers the ground.

During the summer months, the goldfinch's diet includes a variety of other seeds as they ripen, though it prefers those from plants in the daisy family, for example groundsel, dandelion, ragwort and sowthistle early in the summer, hardheads in August, and later still burdock which is an important winter food. The goldfinch is the only bird able to reach the seeds buried in the depths of teasel flower heads; in fact, these seeds are eaten mainly by the male goldfinch which has a slightly longer beak than the female.

Above: Most finches have wing bars, but none are as large and striking as those of the goldfinch. The bright yellow patch is obvious even on perched birds. The goldfinch's scientific name comes from *carduelis* the latin for thistle. The seeds of this plant are the bird's favourite food.

Goldfinch (*Carduelis carduelis*), 12cm (4¾in) from beak to tip of tail. The two sexes are almost identical in colour and size, and there is no distinct winter or summer plumage. Although not thought of as migratory, about three-quarters of British goldfinches leave here usually in October.

143

There is, however, a risk factor: sadly, goldfinches occasionally get trapped by the powerful hooked seed heads of these plants, and die.

Versatile feet The goldfinch uses its feet to hold food while it eats—something that few other birds can do. From a firm perch, the feeding bird pulls a thin seed-bearing stem with its beak and places it under its feet to hold the stem steady while eating the seeds.

A trick commonly taught to goldfinches in the sixteenth century—caught and caged for their colourful plumage and song—involved a repetition of this pull and hold procedure. The birds could only get food and water by pulling the strings of a cart, without letting go, and drawing the cart up a slope.

Song-flights The goldfinch has a pleasant, canary-like, twittering song. You can hear the song throughout the year, but the bird sings most regularly from March to July, either from a perch or in flight. In a display above his territory, the male has a rather hesitant song-flight with deep, slow wing-beats and spread tail. Like other finches, the normal flight is undulating; during this flight the goldfinch often repeats a characteristic 'stickelitt' call.

Building a nest Goldfinch territories are usually small, and several pairs may nest together in a loose colony. The swaying outer branches of large trees, bushes and tall

Above: Goldfinches have long, narrow tweezer-like beaks that can prise open prickly seed heads to extract seeds that other birds cannot reach. Equipped with relatively short, stout legs, goldfinches are acrobatic birds, clinging to swaying plants like tits.

Left: Both parents feed the nestlings on regurgitated seeds and a few insects, often collected some distance away. The mother normally produces two broods a season. The earliest chicks leave the nest in June. In years when the summer is warm and dry and food is abundant, breeding continues into August or even September, enabling a third brood to be raised.

...dges might seem precarious for a nest, but ...e goldfinches favours such sites. In a garden ...e bird often chooses a fruit tree for a nest ...e, but there are no hard and fast rules— ...ything from a full-grown horse chestnut ...ivy on a wall will do.

The nest, immaculately neat and compact, ...d deep enough to retain the eggs and chicks ... windy conditions, is bound firmly to ...anches with spiders' webs. Rootlets, dead ...ass, hair and wool are the usual nesting ...aterials, while wool and fluff from ripe ...eds, especially sallow catkins, are used to ...ake a soft, warm lining. The goldfinch may ...tach moss and lichen to the outside of the ...st. Occasionally these birds make use of ...usual nesting materials. A few years ago, ... East Malling Research Station in Kent, ...e pair of goldfinches carefully untied ...astic labels from trees, and used them to ...ecorate their nest.

Both adults fly to and fro together during ...nstruction of the nest, but only the female ...uilds—the male watches her. The female lays ...bout five or six eggs and does all the in- ...ibating. The male has the task of collecting ...od for himself and his mate at this time so ...e female need leave the nest only to stretch ...er legs, to drink or to preen. The eggs take ...early two weeks to hatch, and the young ...an fly in two to three weeks.

Safety in numbers Like other finches, ...oldfinches are gregarious; breeding pairs ...nd family parties flock together in places ...here food is plentiful, in groups given the ...ttractive name 'charms'. This enables young ...irds to learn where to find food, and offers ...ome protection by virtue of the group's ...arge numbers—many pairs of eyes spot ...anger more easily than one.

Many parents and young birds leave ...Britain, migrating to their wintering grounds ...n Holland, Belgium, western France, Spain ...nd Portugal. Until the end of the nineteenth ...entury, many were trapped on the south ...oast of England as they migrated. Trappers ...sed a cage with an automatic trap door called ... *chardonneret*—from the French for gold- ...inch.

World-wide distribution The absence of ...oldfinches from much of Scotland and their ...carcity in northern England, despite the ...presence of suitable habitats, suggests that ...the climate in these areas is unfavourable to ...the birds. Their natural range extends ...throughout much of Europe, to western ...Asia and North Africa, but not much further ...north than southern Sweden.

Attempts to introduce the species to several ...states in North America have failed, perhaps ...because of competition from the native ...American goldfinch. Nevertheless, it was ...successfully introduced to Bermuda, Austra- ...lia, Tasmania and New Zealand—perhaps too ...successfully in the latter case, where it has ...become something of a pest on strawberry ...farms, nipping seeds from the ripe fruits.

Above: Until they moult in the autumn, the young goldfinches have pale heads without the contrasting red and white pattern of their parents. The young birds also have streaks on their back and flanks, but do not have the same wing-bars as the adults.

Right: The smooth, finely spotted eggs are laid in nests usually 4-15m (13-50ft) above ground. Despite these often dangerous heights, the deep nest provides ample security.

Fitting the bill

The **greenfinch (1)** with its 'general purpose' seed-eating bill tackles small seeds like those of chick-weed and groundsel, or larger seeds such as bramble, sunflower and corn.

A long, thin tweezer-like bill enables the **goldfinch (2)** to delve into the prickly seed heads of thistles and teasels.

The short, round bill of the **bullfinch (3)** is sharp at the edges—ideal for nipping off and then peeling buds.

Only the **hawfinch (4)** with its strong skull and jaw muscles can crack open the large hard seeds of cherries and damsons. These are held between special pads in the massive bill, and crushed slowly—the beak exerts over 45kg (100lb) of pressure.

The upper and lower parts of the **crossbill's (5)** beak twist and cross. This is effective for prising open the scales of spruce and pine cones—the bird then uses its long tongue to scoop out the seeds.

1   sunflower seeds   corn

2   thistle   burdock

3   fruit tree bud   redcurrant

4   rose hip   cherry

5   spruce cone and seed

RESIDENT THRUSHES

The clear, musical, flute-like notes of our thrushes are justly famous. From dawn to dusk on most days of the year you can hear their voices throughout the countryside.

People often think song and mistle thrushes are difficult to separate. Both are immediately recognisable as thrushes, with medium length, fairly stout bills, speckled underparts, brownish upperparts, long legs and rather large eyes. The mistle thrush is slightly longer than the song thrush but there are other differences as well. The upperparts of the song thrush are a warm brown, and those of the mistle thrush a distinctly greyer brown. You can see these features quite clearly when the birds are in flight. As the birds pass overhead, look at the axillaries (the feathers covering the 'armpits'): they are a flaming orange-yellow in the song thrush and white in the mistle thrush. The tail of the song thrush is a uniform brown but the mistle thrush has whitish tips to the outer tail feathers. The underparts differ as well: both birds have dark brown breast spots on a pale background, but the spots of the mistle thrush are bigger, more rounded, and altogether bolder, on a paler background.

Rich song All members of the thrush family sing loud, clear, musical flute-like notes. The special qualities of the song thrush are its vigour and repetition. The bird sings the same notes two, three, even five or six times – sometimes you could swear that it is practising a choice phrase. The song thrush uses favourite note sequences time and time again, interspersed with numerous other notes and phrases, many of them mimicking other birds. Some species, such as the chaffinch, sing rather poorly at the start of the season and their performance steadily becomes more polished, but the song thrush sings well right from the start, and some people think its performance is enriched with age.

The mistle thrush has a more limited song – a sequence of a few notes in permutation. It is loud, clear, full, rich and leisurely, and could be monotonous if it were not for its fine quality.

Right: Song thrushes excel in cracking snail shells and extracting the flesh, thus providing themselves with a valuable source of food when drought drives the worms deeper. They beat the victim against a stone or hard surface ('anvil') to break it.

Mistle thrush

sandy grey back

bold spots on white breast

striking white underwing patches

long wings and tail

white outer tail feathers

Mistle thrush (*Turdus viscivorus*) 27cm (10½in) from beak to tail; distribution widespread in all areas apart from some northern parts of Scotland. Resident.

orange-yellow underwing patches

Song thrush

brown back

Song thrush (*Turdus philomelos*) 23cm (9in) from beak to tail. Resident. Distribution widespread.

Opposite page: A song thrush at its well-hidden nest with young chicks. The chicks take 13 or 14 days to fledge completely.

Above: A juvenile song thrush can be distinguished from an adult by its speckled back plumage. Song thrushes nearly always sing from an elevated song perch.

In most years song thrushes start to sing in November – even October – and do not stop until July or later. The mistle thrush does not start singing until the turn of the year and usually ends at the beginning of June.

The call notes of the two species are quite different. An alarmed song thrush says 'tchouk tchouk . . .', the notes coming faster and closer together when the bird is particularly anxious. The mistle thrush has a loud, vigorous call which sounds rather like a football rattle.

Habitat preferences Although the two species are frequently found in the same acre of ground, they have different habitat preferences. Song thrushes are at home in gardens and shrubberies, and you will probably see more nesting around houses than in farmland. You might hear eight or nine individuals on a half mile walk on a mild November morning, which suggests a density of one bird every hundred yards or so.

Mistle thrushes are always more thinly distributed and seem to require much larger territories. They too penetrate urban areas, but they tend to favour parks, cemeteries, and playing fields rather than gardens. Large mature gardens and parklands, on the other hand, are typical habitats for them. In the breeding season you may find them in woodlands and even conifer plantations, so long as there are grassy rides or adjacent grasslands for spring feeding.

Song thrushes tend to favour the same type of habitat in winter and summer, although the higher ground is vacated before the cold winter weather sets in, and a proportion of the population migrates. In northern Britain the migration is chiefly to Ireland, but those individuals that migrate from the south make chiefly for Iberia. In harsh winters, non-migrating song thrushes [m] suffer so severely that they are obliged [to] carry out a cold-weather movement – emergency migration. The small propor[tion] of song thrushes that migrate usually go [to] France.

Song thrushes are solitary and flock [to]gether only on migration. Mistle thrushes, [on] the other hand, tend to move about in fam[ily] parties at the end of the breeding seas[on]; the parties later amalgamate to form lo[ose] flocks of up to 100 birds which roam [the] countryside together, penetrating even w[ild] upland country in their search for fo[od]. During midwinter the flocks split up and [the] birds occupy their territories for the st[art] of a new breeding season.

Superbly structured nests Mistle thrush[es] tend to start breeding two or three wee[ks] earlier than song thrushes, work on the n[est] often starting before February is out. [In] both species the hen alone builds the ne[st] which is well-engineered and incorpora[tes] grasses and mud for bonding. The nest [of] the song thrush is especially beautifu[l,] smooth, symmetrical, and rather like t[he] inside of a coconut shell.

The song thrush is versatile and adaptab[le] in its choice of nest sites, hiding – or sometim[es] failing to hide – its nest in bushes and shrub[s]. Its willingness to live so close to man enab[les] it to exploit such unlikely sites as the top [of] the cistern in an outside lavatory, althou[gh]

Left: An egg and some chicks of a song thrush. This species is unique amon[g] European birds for its habit of plastering the inside of it[s] nest. The plaster is made from dung or rotten wood mixed with saliva.

Below: A song thrush removing a faecal sac from its young. The parent does this to keep the nest clean, depositing the sac some distance from the nest.

148

...atural sites greatly predominate.

The mistle thrush normally builds its ...est in the fork of a tree, perhaps 7-9m ...0-30ft) up, and remarkably well hidden. ...rom this vantage point the incubating ...male keeps a watchful eye, crouching low if ...he suspects she is being observed. Mistle ...rushes are fearless in the defence of their ...ests and young, and do not hestitate to ...ackle birds much larger than themselves. ...part from egg-stealing members of the ...row family, their chief avian predator, ...nd the song thrush's as well, is the sparrow-...awk. Peregrines occasionally eat them.

There are four or five song thrush eggs ...n a clutch, each a beautiful blue thinly ...peckled with black. They are incubated by ...he hen alone, and take 13-14 days to hatch ...nd a similar period to fledge. A second ...rood is often followed by a third. The ...nistle thrush may lay three to six eggs, ...hough four is normal. Their background ...olour varies from cream to pale greeny-blue, ...nd they are dramatically blotched and speck-...ed with sepia. The incubation period is the ...same as for the song thrush, but the young ...may take a day or two longer to fledge. The ...juveniles develop speckled back plumage ...which they lose when they become fully ...mature by the following spring.

Feeding habits Thrushes feed on fruit for ...much of the year; the rest of the time they ...rely on worms, insects and other invertebrates.

You often see them feeding on lawns: a quick hop forward to focus more accurately, using monocular vision, (not to listen); a few vigorous pecks, and the worm is dragged out. Song thrushes crack snails on their 'anvils' (stones), and during snow cover they ferret about for food in hedge bottoms and even among the marram grass along the coast. Mistle thrushes are more reliant on worms and insects, often feeding in the centre of fields. In a sense the feeding habits sum up the temperaments of the two species: the mistle thrush bold but wary, even self assertive; the song thrush more retiring, and often unobtrusive.

Above: A mistle thrush feeding its young. Fruit is an important part of the diet of both species, but particularly of the mistle thrush which favours mistletoe berries—hence its name. In northern Britain rowan provides tasty berries and even isolated trees far up on the fellsides may be visited and stripped bare. Holly, yew, hawthorn and, later in the winter, rose hips and ivy berries are also eaten by both species.

Identifying songbirds

Redwing

Song thrush

Blackbird ♀

Fieldfare

HARK, HARK, THE LARKS!

The skylark is recognisable for its sustained song as it flies in a broad sweep high over open ground. The rarer woodlark sings as it spirals upwards, its distinctive song a rich and beautiful melody.

The woodlark and skylark have very different distributions within the British Isles. To see a woodlark on any but a few lowland heaths in southern England is enough to turn an ordinary day's bird-watching into a red-letter day. On the other hand, the skylark is the characteristic bird of open country and, according to field work completed in 1972, it is undoubtedly the most widespread breeding bird in Britain and Ireland.

The skylark's brown plumage serves as a good camouflage for the bird when it is in the open ground it prefers. Unlike most birds, it sings on the wing, marking out its territory on the ground by circling and singing above it. Its song, which includes mimicry of the notes

Above: Woodlarks are rare birds and the total British population may now number only 150-200 pairs. They breed only in dry areas of heathland or downland.

Opposite page: Skylark country–open arable fields, hedgerows hed scrub.

Woodlark (*Lullula arborea*), 15cm (6in) long from beak to tail. Distribution southern England and Wales.

Bird song

The skylark (right) is famed for its habit of soaring high in the sky, rising and descending repeatedly, all the time pouring out a torrent of song. The woodlark (far right) has a circular song-flight and its song is mellow-toned. Both birds also sing from song-posts. A singing bird is advertising itself. It is proclaiming that it owns a territory and warning its neighbours that it is around. Birds also sing to find a mate. Females may be attracted to a particular type of songster and, with many species, the unpaired male sings a different song from the male with a mate. Winter song is rare in most birds as there are few species that defend their territories or pair up then.

skylark

woodlark

of other birds, is a familiar and attractive feature of the countryside for much of the year. It is very loud, and a bird which seems to be singing overhead often turns out to be a mere speck in the sky. One singing bird stimulates another: as dawn breaks over an area of downland where there are no larks singing, all the birds start to sing within the space of one minute, producing a complete wall of sound. This habit of singing in flight is crucial to the skylark's ability to colonize truly open areas: other species of open ground are often unable to breed if there are no song-posts from which to sing and mark their territories.

The skylark can often be seen busily peck-ing at apparently bare earth. For most of the year it is mainly vegetarian, feeding on the weed seeds that lie dormant in the ground. At other times, particularly spring when the seeds are beginning to grow, it may feed on the nutritious growing points of the young plant. Because of modern agricultural technique, this has turned the bird into a pest: in the past sugar-beet growers planted the seeds densely in rows, later thinning them. Today farmers have taken to sowing single encapsulated seeds exactly where they want the plants to grow. However, the skylarks may then peck the growing point from the young seedling and spoil the farmer's carefully planned harvest.

Three broods Skylark pairs form during early spring. You often see a singing bird at the end of its song-flight drop to the ground and display to another bird already standing there. The nest is always on the ground, often built into an existing depression such as the hoof-print of a cow. Indeed, some bird-watchers have encouraged skylarks to nest by forming hollows with their heels in firmly rolled grounds.

The nest cup is built of coarse grass and roots lined with fine grass and sometimes hair. The eggs, generally three or four to the clutch, are whitish and thickly speckled all over with olive or brownish markings. The young, which hatch after 11 days incubation, are able to fly at about three weeks old and start to behave more like their parents. They are still easily distinguishable from their parents because of their more blotched and softer brown plumage. A single pair may raise three broods during the breeding season from April to July.

New plumage The only period when skylark song is absent is during the moult in August and early September when young and old alike renew their plumage completely. The young birds lose their soft blotchy plumage and the adults the old, bleached and tattered feathers they have worn for the whole of the preceding year. When the moult is complete, juveniles and adults are indistinguishable. The sexes always look alike, at least to human eyes, but the males average about 6% bigger

Below: The eggs of the skylark hatch after 11 days incubation, and the young remain in the nest for 8-10 days. Then, although they are not yet able to fly, they leave it and move around in the grass. At this stage their bodies are well feathered, but their wings are not yet grown and they still retain some down.

n the females.

During autumn and winter skylarks often ... together in flocks which include young ...ds and immigrants from further afield. ... much of the winter, territorial males can ... heard singing in all but the bleakest areas. ...ly during the period of least daylight does ...g almost cease – presumably since the full ...urs of daylight are needed to find food.

Woodlark There is a marked contrast be-...een the widely distributed and familiar ...lark and the rare and local woodlark ...ich is limited to southern Britain. Although ... woodlark is now a rare bird it was com-...n at the beginning of the 19th century. ... suffered particularly during two cold ...nters in the early 1960s. During the 1970s ...re were many years when none was ...orded but there may now be one or two ...ritories occupied each year. Indeed, since ... study made in 1972 the distribution of the ...ecies has contracted, with the outlying ...pulations in parts of Wales and Lincoln-...re in particular diminishing still further. ...Woodlarks breed only in dry areas of ...athland and downland. They need short ...ss areas for feeding, longer vegetation for ...sting and some vantage points such as ...es, bushes or even fence posts for song-...sts. The woodlark's song is its most ...stinguished attribute – few birds have such ...nelodious and distinctive series of flowing ...tes which may continue, uninterrupted, for ... or 20 minutes at a time.

The woodlark looks fairly similar to the ...ylark but it has a very short tail, (don't ...nfuse it with the tailless, moulting skylark ... late summer), a conspicuous dark brown ...d white mark on the leading edge of the ...osed wing, and a rather finer bill than the ...ylark.

One problem with such a rare species is that ...any inexperienced bird-watchers report tree ...pits as woodlarks. Tree pipits inhabit a ...milar habitat and have a fairly pleasing ...ng, although it is boring and repetitive ...nen compared with a genuine woodlark. ...neir song flights are also quite similar for ...though the woodlark commonly sings from ... song-post, it also sings during its looping ...splay flight.

Breeding woodlarks are often found in ...aditional sites after intervals of several ...ars. This may mean that breeding birds had ...en overlooked in the meantime, but it is ...uch more likely to indicate that woodlarks ...ok for a particular sort of area in which to ...eed.

The first clutch of eggs, usually three or ...ur, is laid at the end of March or early April ...d there may be three broods a year. The ...ung birds leave the nest before they can fly ...d hide singly in the vegetation whilst being ...red for by their parents for a further 10-14 ...ays. Both young and old birds moult in late ...mmer and, in European areas where they ...e more common than in the British Isles,

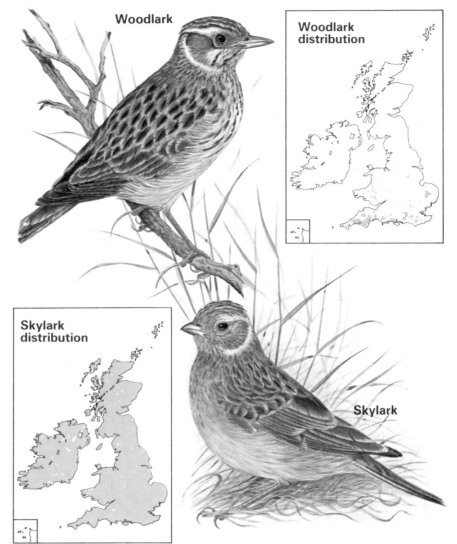

Woodlark

Woodlark distribution

Skylark distribution

Skylark

they can often be found in quite large loosely associated flocks on stubble. The song has ceased by this time, but their distinctive liquid call-note of three syllables – 'ti-loo-whit' – and their short tails identify them.

Skylark pie? With the great interest in bird-watching and bird protection in the 1980s it is amazing to record that less than 100 years ago there was a thriving export trade with France in dead skylarks. They were netted on the south downs and shipped across the Channel to be sold in French markets.

Skylark (*Alauda arvensis*), 18cm (7in) long from beak to tail. Distribution map opposite. Resident, winter migrants from northern Europe.

Below: Skylarks always make their nests on the ground. These nestlings are about two weeks old and are well camouflaged with their soft brown plumage.

Mammals of field and hedgerow

The hedgerows, scrublands, woodland edges and open ground we call the patchwork landscape support a thriving community of mammals, but little has been known about mammals' intimate lives until quite recently. However, close observation has revealed life-styles of great intricacy, and produced some surprises too.

The patchy habitat of fields and hedges created by man suits many mammals admirably. Arable grassland allows rabbits to colonize, while hares are at home in the larger expanses. The areas in between provide an array of nutritious foods–succulent shoots, leaves and bark, seeds, nuts, fungi and berries and, not least, the brimming larder of invertebrate life which fuels shrews, moles, bats and to varying degrees all the more omnivorous mammals. Nevertheless, for small mammals these scrubby oases offer both refuge and risk, for thick undergrowth provides a formidable attack front for weasels and stoats, while out in the open foxes glide silently from one line of cover to the next, feeding on beetles, worms and blackberries if no more solid food is available.

In the last 20 years research has given us many refreshing new perspectives on mammal life. Rabbits, for instance, are shown to do much more than breed and devour grass–they adhere to a strict social code, with elaborate behaviour for signalling status and for wooing mates. To the well-known 'mad March' courtship antics of hares are added intriguing observations on the fleeting but efficient care the doe extends to her new-born young. And the social behaviour of the versatile fox seems endlessly flexible to suit changing conditions.

Most mammals, however, shun company outside the breeding season. Dormice, moles and hares lead essentially solitary lives; shrews too covet their personal space and quarrel endlessly with their neighbours. Among paired weasels and stoats no love is lost between mates, both sexes of which carve out their own home ranges. A patchwork habitat it may be, but every resource is scrupulously parcelled out by rigid territorial behaviour, while the measure of compromise needed for courtship and family life has led to the evolution of subtle diplomacy at all levels.

CHECKLIST

This checklist is a guide to the mammals you will find in fields and hedgerows. Although you will not see them all in the same place, you should be able to spot many of them as you walk through the countryside during the changing seasons. The species listed in **bold** *type are described in detail.*

Badger	Harvest mouse
Bank vole	Hedgehog
Brown hare	**Mole**
Brown rat	Pipistrelle bat
Common shrew	**Pygmy shrew**
Dormouse	**Rabbit**
Field vole	Roe deer
Fox	**Weasel**
Grey squirrel	**Stoat**

Above: The common shrew is a voracious little hunter.

Left: Fox cubs on the lookout for danger before emerging from the shelter of their earth beneath a tree trunk.

WEASEL: SMALL BUT FIERCE CARNIVORE

Although weasels have long been persecuted, they are common today throughout the British Isles. Their fierce, relentless hunting techniques make them deadly enemies of the small rodents that form the bulk of their diet and, since they are strong and bold, they may also take prey larger than themselves.

The weasel is one of Britain's fiercest carnivores. It is sometimes confused with a relative in the mustelid family, the stoat, but it is generally smaller, although a male weasel and female stoat are about equal in size. Both species are similar in coloration, with chestnut-brown backs and white fur on the underside; but whereas stoats have a distinct dividing line between the two colours of the coat, weasels have an uneven margin which is different in every individual. Like that of the stoat, the tail of a weasel is short and bushy and the same colour as the back, but it lacks the stoat's black tip.

Weasels have long, slender bodies and short limbs, ideal for squeezing down mouse holes and mole runs, and into crevices in walls, to search for prey. The head is small and bluntly pointed, with small rounded ears. Weasels are found throughout mainland Britain, and on Anglesey, Skye and the Isle of Wight. They are not found in Ireland, but stoats are, and are known as 'weasels' in that country because they are smaller than the stoats found in mainland Britain.

Persecution Like all carnivores, weasels have long been persecuted by man, and they are still regarded as vermin by gamekeepers. Certainly they will take the eggs and young of some birds, and they raid chicken runs, but studies have shown that the value of weasels to farmers and foresters far outweighs these occasional depredations. During a year a family of weasels may account for 2000 or more destructive small rodents, especially mice and voles.

When rabbits were trapped on a commercial scale, weasels and stoats were often incidentally caught in gin traps and, during the 1950s, the populations of both mustelids declined. Today they are more abundant, and, when trapping does take place, more humane traps are used. Experienced trappers take advantage of the weasel's habit of hunting along natural boundary lines, such as walls and hedges, and set their traps in the cracks and crevices the animals like to explore.

Quick hunters Weasels are quick-moving, agile, relentless hunters. They patrol their territory at regular intervals, mostly at night but often during the day as well, running with their bodies held low or bounding along with their backs arched. Mice and voles are often pursued down into their underground runs. Occasionally weasels run along the tops of walls or hedges in search of birds and their nests. They hunt mainly by scent, stopping from time to time to stand on their hind legs to test the air and survey their surroundings.

Prey is killed quickly, with a bite to the back of the head. Animals such as rabbits and large birds are subdued by repeated attacks to the throat and major blood vessels. Weasels eat almost any animal that they can overcome and kill, from small rodents to shrews, frogs, birds and their eggs and even fish. They swim after water voles, and

WEASEL (*Mustela nivalis*)
Size Highly variable. Head and body 17-22cm (6½-8½in) plus tail 4-7.5cm (1½-3in). Adult weight 90-170g (3-6oz). Males are larger and heavier than females.
Colour Chestnut brown above, white below—similar to stoat but lacking the even margin between the brown back and white underside.
Breeding season from March to September.
Gestation period 6 weeks.
No of young 2 litters of 3-8 young per year.
Lifespan 3-4 years in the wild, up to 10 years in captivity.
Food Carnivorous. Mice, voles, rats, moles, shrews, rabbits, birds, frogs, toads, insects, reptiles.
Predators Man—trapping. Larger mammals, hawks.
Distribution All over mainland Britain.

Opposite page: The alert, wide-awake expression is characteristic of the weasel.

Below: The weasel kills its prey by a sharp bite on the back of the victim's neck.

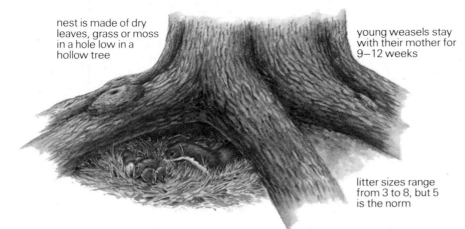

nest is made of dry leaves, grass or moss in a hole low in a hollow tree

young weasels stay with their mother for 9–12 weeks

litter sizes range from 3 to 8, but 5 is the norm

Above: A weasel's nest. The female has two litters a year – one in April or May and the other in September. You'll find weasels in many habitats, ranging from woodland, farmland, hedgerows and moorland to mountains and even urban areas.

Below: Weasels are inquisitive animals, relying largely on scent to help them in their hunting. They are not very vocal. When they are alarmed they hiss and, if provoked, will give a short screaming bark. In captivity they remain very aggressive and will hiss, bark and snap at the slightest provocation.

occasionally take carrion. Excess food is sometimes stored in or near their underground dens. Dens containing the remains of up to 50 small rodents have been discovered.

Competition-free diet Weasels and stoats, with such a diversity of sizes ranging from the tiny female weasel at 23cm (9in) to the 40cm (16in) long male stoat, are thought by some ecologists to exhibit the phenomenon of 'character displacement'. They are all carnivores and therefore potential competitors, but, since they are in three size groups, they can often divide up the available food resources and thus avoid too much competition. At the two extremes of the range, the female weasel and male stoat are specialist predators on small rodents and large prey respectively. The female weasel feeds almost exclusively on mice and voles, while the male stoat is capable of killing prey up to the size of a large rabbit. The male weasel and female

stoat, of roughly equal size, fall between the two categories and feed mainly on medium sized prey animals.

The weasel population fluctuates with abundance of food, particularly mice a voles. A weasel may live in a locality u almost all the rodents in an area of 180-27 (600-900ft) across are eliminated, bef moving to a new home.

Separate territories Weasels are found almost any habitat that has sufficient fc and shelter. They are, of course, most co mon where the greatest concentrations mice and voles are found. They also live and around farm buildings, in park land among stones and rubble on derelict land.

Males and females have separate territori varying in size according to the abundance prey. Males usually have larger territor than females and mark them with scent fr musk glands beneath the tail. This scen also released when an animal is frightened disturbed and, as with most members of Mustelidae, it is very pungent.

Weasels do not make regular runw within their territories, but they often use runs and burrows of small rodents for th own shelter or den, and may sleep off a he; meal in the home of a recent victim.

Two litters In Britain the weasel usually I two breeding seasons a year. The first beg in March and the young are born in April a May. The second may involve males a females born during the spring season, a continues until September. The seasons be; when males leave their territories to finc female in oestrus. It is thought that the mt glands may be used to attract males a

Weasel lore

For centuries the weasel has been attributed with magical properties. A 12th century bestiary say that weasel mothers can bring their dead young to life; weasels were said to drink the blood of their victims, a belief that probably arose from their habit of killing by a sharp bite on the neck and gripping tightly until the prey dies. They are also supposed to hypnotize their prey by 'dancing' before it. Their playful habits elicit mobbing behaviour from small birds, some of which come too close and become victims. It is unlikely that 'dancing' is hunting technique used by many weasels, but a few may learn that it attracts prey.

males to each other. Unlike some mustelids, including the stoat, weasels do not show the phenomenon of delayed implantation, and the young are born six weeks after mating. The female nurses the young for four or five weeks, and if she is disturbed during this time will move them to a new nest site. The male weasel plays no part in rearing the young.

Family groups After weaning the mother continues her parental care by teaching her offspring to hunt and kill. Their education begins when the female brings back injured and disabled prey to the nest, but within a short time she takes them on hunting excursions throughout her territory.

The young remain with their mother for two to three months, by which time they can fend for themselves and their mother is involved with raising another litter. At this stage in their lives the young are at their most vulnerable and in looking for territories of their own many fall vicitim to traps or natural enemies such as owls, hawks and domestic cats. Their inquisitive natures can often prove fatal: their habit of bolting into a crevice when disturbed, to emerge after a few moments to investigate the cause of the disturbance, can have fatal results when the intruder is a gamekeeper with a gun.

Young from the second litter often stay with their mother for longer than three months and the family may not break up until the start of the breeding season the following year. Such family groups share the same territory, but may not necessarily keep together when foraging, and individual weasels may be scattered over a wide area. Occasionally, especially in winter, several family groups combine to form a pack of as many as 30 individuals.

Weasel parasites A number of parasites are found on weasels, and also fleas, which are commonly transmitted from their rodent prey. There is also a biting louse, *Trichodectes mustelae*, that is found only on weasels. The nematode worm *Skrjabingylus nasicola* is found in weasels' nasal passages and damages the bones and skull, although apparently causes no distress nor results in death.

Above: When moving, weasels look snake-like, and it was once thought that a weasel could squeeze through a wedding ring without difficulty. Such an event is unlikely, but it is true that the skull of a female weasel can be passed through a standard ring 2cm (¾in) in diameter.

Below: A young weasel. Mortality during the first year is high and few weasels survive to the maximum expected lifespan of four years in the wild.

THE STOAT: A WINTER TURNCOAT

One of our smallest but most bloodthirsty carnivores, the stoat is the only mammal in the British Isles which regularly kills prey that is much heavier than itself (rabbits, for example). In the north of Britain the stoat turns white in winter and is then known as the ermine.

Below: A stoat in full winter coat. This is the only one of the mustelid group of mammals in Britain (a group which includes the badger, polecat, pine marten and weasel) to change its coat colour with the seasons in this way.

160

e stoat is one of a number of highly nivorous, sinuous-bodied mammals which grouped together in the family Mustelie. With its long, slim, muscular body, short s, bluntly pointed head, and small rounded s, the stoat closely resembles its relative weasel – indeed, in Ireland it is often called easel. It is distinguished from the weasel by larger size and by its proportionately ger, black-tipped tail. However, size is not very good way of distinguishing between ats and weasels, particularly in the wild, en they are usually only glimpsed fleetingly d at a considerable distance.

Male stoats are much larger than the males. This disparity in size enables the es to seek different food; the female being aller, needs less food to sustain herself, d, because of her small size, is more icient at hunting small prey, such as field les, which she can follow along their runs. e bigger male seeks a wider range of prey.

A change of coat A stoat moults its coat ice a year: the winter moult starts in tober and the spring moult in mid-bruary. In northern Britain the stoat turns ite in winter except for the black tip of its l. In the south the winter coat is the same lour as the summer coat, or perhaps a little ler, but it is much thicker and warmer. ere is a small intermediate zone in northern gland where stoats with both types of nter coat occur, and some with coats that rn white in patches. These differences in the lour of the winter coat are related to the onthly minimum temperatures, and also the number of days on which snow falls d the length of time it lies on the ground. male stoats whiten more easily than the ales, probably because their smaller size, d consequently greater surface area in lation to weight, make them more suscept-le to cold.

White stoats hunting on snow free ground e, however, very conspicuous, especially as ey rush about in search of prey and equently stand up on their hind legs to look ound. But it seems that the loss of hunting ficiency during intermittent thaws, or on ow free ground, is outweighed by the dvantage that their white camouflage coat ves them in snowy conditions.

Habitat and distribution The stoat is at ome in almost any environment, from salt arshes and coastal sand dunes to the tops of ountains – it has been seen at the ob-ervatory on top of Ben Nevis. Within these verse habitats, the density of the stoat opulation is governed by the availability of ood, which is obviously more abundant in ch and varied woodland than on rocky llsides.

With the possible exception of the fox, the oat is the most widely distributed British rnivore – it occurs throughout mainland ritain; however, there are areas in the west nd north-west of Scotland where stoats are

Four small carnivores

Polecat

distinctive face markings

Pine marten
pale throat patch

bushy tail

Stoat

black tip   intermediate winter coat

Weasel
short tail

STOAT (*Mustela erminea*).
Size Male about 30cm (11½in) in length; female 26cm (10in).
Weight Male about 300g (10½oz); female about 200g (7oz).
Habitat Found in almost all habitats throughout Britain. Commonest where prey is most abundant.
Breeding Mates in summer, delayed implantation, 6–13 young, born April/May.
Food Birds, voles, rabbits, rats.
Moults Twice annually, white in winter in Scotland.

absent or extremely rare. These are areas where there are no rabbits, or only very few. Most of the larger Scottish islands have a stoat population, but there are no stoats on Orkney and those on Mull belong to a slightly different Irish race.

Hunting and killing A male stoat hunts over much larger areas than a female – the average home range of a male is between 10 and 200 hectares (25-500 acres), while that of the smaller female is between 7 and 45 hectares (17-100 acres). Except when young are being reared, the sexes hunt and live separately. The animal does not use all of its home range at one time – it hunts over a small area for a few days and then moves on. For this reason

Above: The pine marten, the largest of these four similar-looking carnivores is about the size of a domestic cat, at 44-50cm (16-20in) long, while the weasel, the smallest, is only 17-22cm (7-9in) in length. The females of all four species are, however, considerably smaller than the males.

Below: Stoats are not as closely tied to dense cover as weasels and may sometimes be seen in fields away from hedges or walls.

it has several dens, in which it lies up and rests, scattered throughout the area in which it is active. The stoat tends to hunt along walls, hedges and ditches which provide it with cover and also harbour its prey.

The stoat hunts both by day and by night, but with peaks of activity. When hunting it uses its senses of smell and sight, both of which are highly developed. It is a versatile hunter, feeding upon birds and field voles as well as on rabbits—the female stoat taking more voles and small prey than the larger male. The stoat is, in fact, the only British carnivore which regularly kills prey much larger than itself; the rabbit, which is a very important element of its diet, weighs six times as much as a stoat. It also eats rats, which weigh twice as much as the stoat and are powerful adversaries when cornered. When food is scarce the stoat eats items as varied as juniper berries, insects, lizards and frogs.

The stoat kills rabbits by repeated bites on the back of the neck, inflicted while it clings to its victim's back. These bites do not penetrate the spinal cord, nor do they immediately sever major arteries or nerves, so the rabbit dies slowly—it may take a stoat more than ten minutes to dispatch a victim.

Rabbits sometimes sit and watch while a stoat kills one of their number. Mountain hares—the stoat's largest prey—also sit at their burrow entrances or in their forms, apparently unconcerned, as a stoat hunts among them. This behaviour may not be as foolhardy as it seems, for the stoat follows an animal which it has already attacked and weakened in preference to any other.

Above: Like many other carnivores, stoats indulge in 'surplus killing'—killing more prey than they need—if confronted by captive birds. They begin to eat the bird from the neck and work towards the shoulders.

Below: This stoat is in its summer coat—the brown upperparts sharply divided from the yellowish-white underparts. In the background is one of its many dens.

As a killer of birds the stoat is much m[ore] efficient. Its slightly curved canine teeth p[ro]ject well beyond the first cheek teeth, a[nd] these, in turn, are smaller than the second a[nd] third, thus forming a semi-circular prof[ile]. This provides powerful gripping and punct[ur]ing equipment with which the stoat c[an] quickly kill or disable a bird by severing [the] jugular vein and sometimes its caro[tid] arteries.

Stoats at play Stoats are reputed to attr[act] birds within striking distance by what [is] sometimes called dancing. However, this [is] probably just one form of play, althou[gh] stoats have been known to kill birds und[er] these circumstances. Typically, play amo[ng] a young family of stoats includes runni[ng] backwards and forwards, bouncing off fe[nce] posts and small trees, and sudden turns a[nd] changes of direction, all executed at gr[eat] speed. Family groups of young stoats m[ay] sometimes persist into the winter, giving r[ise] to stories of stoats hunting in packs.

Breeding Stoats mate in summer, but t[he] fertilised eggs do not develop immediatel[y] they remain dormant within the female f[or] several months. This means that young [fe]male stoats can be mated before they lea[ve] the nest, thus ensuring that all dispersi[ng] females, of whatever age, are likely to [be] pregnant.

Gestation lasts three to four weeks and t[he] one litter of six to thirteen young is born [in] the following April or May. The young a[re] born blind, helpless and covered with fi[ne] white hair. They are weaned at about fi[ve] weeks and can hunt for themselves when thr[ee] months old.

Stoats and man Stoats are unpopular wi[th] gamekeepers and poultry farmers. Howeve[r,] they do keep down agricultural pests such [as] rabbits and rats. They also limit the field v[ole] population, which might otherwise becom[e] large enough to cause severe damage to tree[s.] But, apart from man, the stoat has no natur[al] predators.

FIELD VOLES: FOOD FOR ALL

The field vole (below), a grassland rodent with a shaggy greyish-brown coat, is a little larger than a mouse, and breeds prolifically – a necessity since it is a major source of food for every bird of prey and carnivorous mammal in Britain.

The field vole is a specialist grass eater. But grass is difficult to digest and is not very nutritious, so the vole must spend a lot of time eating. It feeds by day and night, being most active near dawn and dusk. It is equipped with special teeth to cope with tough grass fibres. The four chisel-edged incisor teeth are used to nip off a grass stem and bite it into short lengths, and the 12 flat-topped cheek-teeth to chew the grass up thoroughly before it is swallowed. Since grass stems and leaves contain abrasive silica, the teeth wear down quickly, but they continue growing throughout the field vole's life.

Long grass hideout Other specialist grazing mammals, such as the rabbit and deer, come

a plentiful food supply while remaining s[...] from predators.

The field vole needs fairly tall grass if [...] above-ground runs are to be sufficien[...] hidden, so it avoids mown grass and close[...] grazed fields. Its favourite habitats are ro[...] side verges, waste land and rough fie[...] where the grass is long and tussocky. A [...] area of long grass in Britain will have fi[...] voles—from moorland over 1200m (4000ft)[...] coastal salt marshes and sand dunes.

Field voles do not live in woodland. [...] new forestry plantations, where the trees ha[...] not grown tall enough to shade and kill [...] grass, are a real haven for them. They son[...] times nibble the bark of the young trees a[...] can do a fair amount of damage in pla[...] ations.

Nesting and breeding Female voles ma[...] breeding nests in spring and summer. T[...] first litter—of four to six babies—is usua[...] born in April. A female can continue pr[...] ducing a new litter every six to eight week[...] right through the summer. The baby vol[...] weaned at 14-28 days old, are able to bre[...] when they are six weeks old, although tho[...] born in late summer wait until the followi[...] spring before starting to reproduce.

Predator pressure Voles must breed pr[...] lifically since it is their only solution to t[...] problem of predation. No other mamm[...] prey is eaten in such huge numbers as t[...] vole. It is hunted by birds of prey, ow[...]

Above: Young field voles, born blind, are only relatively secure from predators in their nest of dried grass. This nest, for instance, was dug out by a dog. Carnivores such as foxes would have little difficulty in locating the nest and eating its inhabitants.

out to feed in full view. If danger threatens, a rabbit can escape down a nearby burrow, while a deer depends on its size and speed for safety. Field voles, however, which cannot run very fast and do not always make underground burrows, have a different strategy for avoiding danger while feeding. They stay hidden in the shelter of long grass, feeding in runways at ground level. In winter, a covering of snow gives even more protection: the voles stay in their runs beneath the snow, enjoying

Looking at vole runways

Field vole runways look like well-worn, mouse-sized paths threading a passage between long grass stems. Those in use have fresh droppings—soft green ovals—scattered along their length. Small piles of 'kibblings'—bits of nibbled grass—mark the places where the voles were feeding. The runs remain visible for some weeks, after voles finish using them. Long grass is essential to provide concealment from predators.

The runways usually radiate out from grass tussocks where the vole has sited its nest. This—made of finely shredded dry grass—must be warm and dry. If a grass tussock does not give enough protection, the vole may dig a shallow burrow, or nest in a hollow under a log or stone. Sometimes it may even make use of corrugated iron roofing sheets which have been discarded from farm buildings and left lying around in a corner of waste land. The corrugations make an excellent waterproof roof for the nest. If you approach a sheet of corrugated iron quietly and lift it quickly, you are almost sure to see a field vole dashing for cover.

Nests are built all year round. Even when there are no young, the adults still need a warm place to sleep. Individuals usually spend their whole lives within 27m (30yd) of the nest, feeding and breeding.

Owls, with their especially efficient night sight, are well-equipped to hunt field voles.

Foxes seem to prefer field voles to other prey, whether eating them at once or burying them to eat later on.

droppings

nest

ats, weasels, foxes, badgers, pine martens, dcats and snakes. Short-eared owls eat most nothing else, and kestrels too are avid d vole hunters, specialising in patrolling e motorway verges which have become the les' favourite habitat. Many of these dators seem to show a particular preference for voles over other prey species.

Plague populations Fast breeding is a remarkably effective way of combating predation. Despite the great numbers of voles ught and eaten by predators each year, eir populations can still increase. The usual ttern is for the vole population to build up high numbers over a few years, then drop. Sometimes, however, plague proportions e reached. An early description of this tails what happened in a part of Essex 400 ars ago: 'About Hallowtide last past 580), in the marishes of Danesie Hundred, a place called Southminster, in the Countie Essex, a strange thing happened: there ddenlie appeared an infinite multitude of ice, which, overwhelming the whole earth the said marishes, did sheare and gnaw the asse by the roots, spoiling and tainting the me with their venemous teeth, in such sort at the cattell which grased thereon were itten with a murreine, and died thereof; hich vermine by policie of man could not be stroied, till now at last it came to passe that ere flocked together all about the same arishes such a number of owles as all the ire was not able to yield; whereby the arsh holders were shortlie deliuered from e vexation of the said mice.' (Holinshed's hronicle, 1586).

This is a remarkably accurate description f what happens during a vole plague – though the cattle probably died of starvation since vole teeth are not venomous. The wls which arrived in such numbers were ort-eared owls, a species which hunts in aylight.

Aggression and stress High vole populations an cause considerable damage and much search has been done into the probable auses of population fluctuation. It often ems to happen in a cycle, a high vole opulation building up every fourth or fifth ear.

At the end of the last century, a Government enquiry blamed vole plagues in Scotland n the gamekeepers who killed the natural redators of the vole. But the explanation for ole plagues is not as simple as that. It is true hat, when the vole population is high, redators move in and concentrate on hunting voles which become very easy to catch, specially if they have eaten most of the grass hich should conceal them. But the fall in umbers often happens more quickly than an be explained by predator hunting alone.

It seems that at high densities the voles' ehaviour changes. They are normally fairly ggressive towards strangers and spend their vhole lives in small areas. As the numbers rise

and crowding occurs, aggression increases; this can take the form of much high-pitched squeaking or chattering when two individuals meet. At the same time, the voles stop breeding as successfully – possibly due to the stress of increased aggression – and numbers start to drop.

The year following the drop in numbers, voles are fairly scarce. But there are still many predators about – those which moved in and bred prolifically when the voles were common. Although the predators turn to other prey, or move to other areas, they probably keep the low vole population in check for some time. Then, as the predators decline and the overgrazed grass recovers, the voles lose some of their aggression and start breeding rapidly again. The next vole plague is under way.

Habitat boom Thousands of years ago, before Man cleared the forests from most of Britain, field voles probably had fewer suitable grassy areas to inhabit. They would have lived in wetter areas where trees could not grow, or in coastal grasslands, and their habitats would have been small and scattered. It is possible that the regular massive increase in vole population which occurs today happens only because man has created much larger areas of land suitable to the vole's way of life.

On the Continent, the field vole's grassland habitat is shared with the common vole.

Although mainly active at night, the field vole is also out and about during the day. When its usual food – grass – is scarce, the field vole will eat bark, bulbs, roots and even fungi.

FIELD VOLE (*Microtus agrestis*); also called short-tailed vole.
Size very variable; adult head-and-body length about 9-13cm (3½-5in); tail 3-4cm (1-1½in). Weight about 20g (¾oz).
Colour greyish-brown above, pure grey underneath. Coat rather shaggy.
Breeding season starts in April, continues throughout summer.
Gestation period About 21 days.
No of young 4-6 per litter.
Lifespan One year, sometimes two.
Food grass stems, green leaves.
Predators birds of prey, carnivorous mammals, snakes.
Distribution everywhere on British mainland, absent from Ireland.

SHREWS: BRITAIN'S SMALLEST MAMMALS

The smallest mammal found in the British Isles is the pygmy shrew, which is half the size of its relative the common shrew. Both these diminutive species are found in Great Britain, but the pygmy shrew also occurs in Ireland where it has been given the name 'dolly-mouse'.

Below: A common shrew. These tiny mammals are extremely prolific—a female bears five to seven young in a litter and may have as many as five litters in one season. However, shrews rarely live beyond the age of 15 months.

although called 'shrew-mice' in the country, the pygmy shrew and the common shrew are not rodents like mice and rats, but insectivores, a group that also contains the hedgehog and the mole. Both species are quite common although they are seldom seen for they stay well hidden in the undergrowth.

Both common and pygmy shrews favour habitats with long vegetation where they can hunt at ground level and not be seen by predators such as owls. Rough grassland, hedgerows and nettlebeds are favoured places. Shrews are especially common in young forestry plantations. In summer a Welsh plantation can have over 14 per acre, which is about twice the number that live in rough grassland. In most parts of mainland Britain, common shrews are five to ten times as abundant as pygmy shrews.

Common shrews make shallow runways in leaf litter and ground vegetation and tunnels through soil that are small in size and flat in cross-section. The pygmy shrew can also dig and burrow with its nose and front paws, but because of its tiny size it can also use holes and tunnels made by other animals such as beetles.

Carnivorous insectivores Shrews are called insectivores but they also eat other small animals, such as spiders and woodlice, as well as insects. Almost any living creature that is small enough is food for a shrew. Shrews hunt by bustling about at ground level, through their runways and down their shallow burrows, sticking their long snouts with sensitive whiskers into every crevice. They are constantly active and inquisitive. When the shrew finds a small creature, it gives the prey a quick sniff, grabs it in its jaws and crunches it up. Common shrews eat quite large snails and earthworms, which are too big for pygmy shrews. Both species eat woodlice, spiders and beetles.

Dr Pernetta, a researcher at Oxford University, found that pygmy shrews are not very fussy about their food – except that they never eat millipedes. Other small invertebrates were eaten in proportion to how many occurred at ground level. Common shrews also dislike millipedes, but spend more time hunting below ground level where they find worms and soil-dwelling insect grubs and larvae.

Food – a time-consuming affair A shrew needs large amounts of food at short, regular intervals. With such a tiny body, the surface area is large in proportion to its weight, and heat is easily lost. So the shrew must eat lots of food to convert into energy sufficient to keep its body temperature at about 37°C (98.4°F). In order to achieve this the shrew must eat every two or three hours or it dies. A typical day for a shrew consists of ten shifts, each about 1¾ hours in length, hunting for food. Between each burst of feeding activity there is a rest of about 45 minutes. It is a round-the-clock cycle, although the greatest active feeding behaviour takes place during the night.

Each day a common shrew eats almost its own weight in food, and a female suckling her young needs one and a half times her own weight. Pygmy shrews require even more food – they lose more heat because their surface area to volume ratio is greater and so they need to eat over twice their own weight in a day to keep active.

Life and death In autumn shrews grow a thick coat to help them survive the winter. However, the winter months are a difficult time for shrews since insects are inactive and other invertebrates are difficult to find. As a result many shrews die as they are unable

Above: Nose to the ground. The pygmy shrew, like all shrews, has a long sensitive snout with fine whiskers. It uses its nose to find food that includes not only insects but any animal that is small enough to eat, such as beetles, woodlice and spiders.

Shrew and mouse line-up

Compared with mice, both common and pygmy shrews are tiny. The common shrew is just over twice the weight of a pygmy shrew but is less than half the weight of a house mouse.

House mouse

Common shrew

Pygmy shrew

THE MADNESS OF THE MARCH HARE

The brown hare is a highly excitable and eccentric animal which, particularly in spring, can behave quite strangely. There is in fact sound evidence to suggest a behavioural basis for the expression 'as mad as a March hare' – the courting instinct of the brown hare is responsible for much of its March madness.

The hare lives out in the open from the moment of birth. To keep warm it has a thick coat, which is white on the underside and a reddish brown above, flecked with tawny gold, black and white to camouflage it. Like a rabbit it has a sensitive nose and a split or hare-lip.

...res are not as a rule sociable, but they do ...ow an intense, if sporadic, interest in each ...er during the mating season. Groups of ...dividuals, consisting of several males called ...k-hares, will pursue a female (doe) in a ...aotic, free-for-all display. During their ...pute over the doe the jacks have boxing ...tches. They rise up on their hind legs, box ...d batter each other with their forepaws and ...n in circles with their hind legs thumping ...e ground.

The display is reminiscent of kangaroos, ...ich indulge in a similar fighting ritual. ...ither hares nor kangaroos, however, kick ...th their hind legs which are extremely ...werful and have long sharp claws that ...uld inflict a fatal injury. In general the ...ntestants box until one backs down, but ...cks have been known to fight to the death.

...one incident in the West Country, the ...ctor broke its opponent's neck with a chop ...ck with its hind paw and then beat the body ...th its forepaws as if it were a drum.

...Jack and doe may also have heated and ...cious arguments. The jack will court a doe ...gardless of whether or not she is in season. ...the jack is too persistent, however, the doe ...ll box at him. As he makes his approach, ...e doe rises up on her hind legs and tries to ...ep head and shoulders above him; in this ...ay she can box down at him to prevent any ...tempt he makes at mating. If that does not ...t him off, she will set upon the jack and bite ...m hard. He may well retaliate, and the fur ...ll really fly until the jack backs off or the doe ...n make her escape.

Breeding behaviour The jack-hare is ready ...mate before the doe–in early January, well ...efore the traditional mad March–and con-...nues through to September. He roams large ...reas of the countryside in search of a doe and, ...hen he finally finds one, has quite a job ...ersuading her to mate. Courtship technique ...very much like that of a buck (male) rabbit; ...e jack pursues his female everywhere. He ...as to compete in a boxing match with others ...r the same doe; but even when he has won ...doe he seldom stays with her for more than a ...ay or two. This is, however, often long ...nough to ensure successful mating.

The jack then continues his roaming exist-...nce in search of more females. By contrast ...he doe has a more settled life. Preliminary ...tudies have shown that she has a fixed ...ome range–known in some counties as ...muese–in which she rears her family. The ...rst litter is usually born at the end of Feb-...uary and the last as late as mid-October. ...itter sizes increase through the season, ...robably as a direct result of more food being ...vailable.

Birth The exact process of birth has always ...een a mystery. It was once believed that a ...are gave birth to one leveret at a time each ...n a different form–the name given to a shal-...ow depression usually in long grass, heather ...r rushes, which passes for the hare's nest.

Boxing hares
In March and April brown hares career around the countryside apparently oblivious of danger. The jacks compete for the favours of the doe in a spectacular courtship ritual in which they fight by rising on their hind legs and boxing each other kangaroo-style.

However a recent film showed that the doe has all her young in one place and moves them to different forms, often some distance apart, after a few days. A Dutch zoologist, Dr. Broekhuizen, has discovered much about the next stages of a leveret's life from his studies on the brown hare in the Netherlands. In his early research, carried out mainly during daylight, he seldom observed the doe paying any attention to her offspring at all. Later he switched to night observation using spot-lights, and discovered that about an hour after sunset the mother hare visited in turn each of her offspring hidden in its form.

The extent of the doe's maternal care is limited to one short suckling period lasting a maximum of three minutes per visit. Perhaps the most interesting behaviour revealed by this research was that a doe may suckle young other than her own. This happens when the leverets are two or three weeks old and begin-ning to be more adventurous. Quite often two or three gang up together from different families in the neighbourhood. But as long as one leveret in the group is hers, a mother will not begrudge feeding both her own and those of her neighbour.

Chances of survival From the moment of

The hare's large eyes have a very glassy quality which enhances the idea that there is madness in the stare. The eyes are on the side of the head and so give good wide-field vision; they can also look backwards. Sometimes, when being chased, the hare will run straight into a net or other object, since it suffers from a blind spot immediately in front.

Comparing the hare with the rabbit

Brown Hare

- long ears with black tips
- large nose
- black top to the tail
- white underside of tail very visible
- very long back legs

Rabbit

- short ears
- back legs shorter than those of the hare

At first glance it is easy to mistake a hare for a rabbit, particularly at a distance. The best way to tell the difference is by the hare's longer, black-tipped ears, and longer, more muscular hind legs. Both hares and rabbits have a split lip, or hare-lip, although there are slight differences. A rabbit's top lip is split up to the nostrils, but has a layer of skin (membrane) to cover the gums. A hare's top lip is split so that the gums are visible. As a result, the top 'buck' teeth may protrude, particularly in old age.

birth, hares live out in the open. For the first weeks of their life, the leverets' instinct is to lie completely still in their 'milking forms'. Like most mammals born in the open, leverets have a coat of fur and are soon fully mobile. This is in complete contrast to rabbits, which are born naked, blind and helpless in the security of a burrow. Leverets have no such security and have to be fully prepared for life in the open.

They soon start to move about to feed and at this stage may fall victim to foxes, stoats and buzzards. Rabbits also are said to kill leverets by biting them on the back of the head. This may be an old wives' tale; but as buck rabbits often kill young rabbits in their warren, they might do the same to young leverets if they came across them. Something like 50% of leverets die before they are a month old, because of predators and the effects of exposure. Does have several litters a year to compensate for this rate of mortality.

To escape from predators the adult hare relies on its highly sensitive hearing to pick up the sound of any approaching danger a long way off. Keeping a sharp watch it will then run away as fast as possible if danger threatens. A rabbit, however, does not detect predators until they are much nearer–and doesn't need to because its burrow is usually only a short dash away. Since the hare's hind legs are much longer and more muscular than those of a rabbit they can power a hare to

35 miles per hour and enable it to jump a height of 2m (6½ft). The hare tends to move in a leapfrog motion with its hind legs landing in front of its forelegs. This is particularly pronounced at speed, when the stride may be as much as 4.5m (15ft). The hare's heart is very strong (much stronger than a rabbit's) and this certainly contributes to its phenomenal stamina. A hare can run up to four miles without tiring; it can also swim if it has to.

Tracks and signs The hare's tracks are easily recognisable by the long prints made by the hind legs and the smaller, rounded foreleg prints. The larger size of these tracks distinguishes them from a rabbit's. If the prints are fresh and clear, you can see four toe prints on the forepaws and four on the hind paws. Droppings are also a familiar sign and are similar to, but larger than, a rabbit's. In some cases they are paler and more fibrous.

The hare is usually a silent animal, although you may hear one emit a scream like that of a child in terror: this cry is given by a leveret in distress, and will immediately bring any doe with leverets running to the scene. An adult hare in pain makes a similar cry.

Night assemblies In areas like Norfolk and Cambridgeshire hares are particularly abundant, and some East Anglian farmers have reported large gatherings of hares–hare parliaments–at night; up to 20 hares have been seen sitting motionless in a circle under the moonlight. In one case, two hares moved

BROWN HARE (*Lepus capensis*). Also known as common hare
Weight of male (jack or buck) averages 3.6kg (8lb), 5kg (11lb) max. Female (doe or jill) slightly more
Length (nose to tail) 55cm (22in)
Colour basically brown, flecked with tawny, yellow gold, generally white underneath
Breeding season early Jan to September
Gestation 42-44 days
No of young (leverets) 3-5
Lifespan average 2½ years, exceptionally 12-13 years
Food diet of grass and cereal crops, mushrooms and shoots; re-ingests droppings
Predators farmers, foxes, stoats, birds of prey
Distribution farmland in Britain and Northern Ireland. Occasionally among sand dunes and woodland

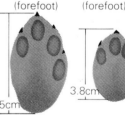

Hare track (forefoot)   **Rabbit track** (forefoot)

5cm   3.8cm

usually only four of the hare's five toes show on the track

Left: Hares move across the ground in a leapfrog motion which is particularly noticeable when they are travelling at speed.

...dden in their form, a ...llow depression in long ...ss, these three leverets ...absolutely still; being ...rn in the open they have ...e choice if they are to ...cape the notice of foxes, ...mestic cats, or birds of ...y flying overhead.

...the centre of the ring and boxed each other ...front of the members of the parliament. The ...gnificance of this is not fully understood, ...ut it does support the theory that hares are ...ssentially nocturnal animals, particularly ...uring the mating season (when these parlia-...ents take place).

Hares certainly feed a lot at night, when ...ey are in less danger of being shot by man. ...ou can see hares out feeding in the fields at ...ight if there is a full moon, which for many ...eople explains the hare's madness. Accord-...g to folklore anyone who stays out under a ...ull moon will go mad (the word lunatic ...omes from the latin word *luna*, meaning ...oon); hence the hare must be mad. It has ...een pointed out that if you turn the moon ...pside down in your imagination, the 'man ...the moon' becomes a hare.

'Hareports' Perhaps the hares' most extra-...rdinary behaviour has been seen at airports. ...everal times over the last decade, large ...umbers of hares have been reported at ...eathrow and Gatwick airports, living on the ...rass alongside the runways; there are similar ...eports from airports all over Europe. It ...eems totally out of character that animals ...ith very sensitive hearing could live in such ...n ear-shattering environment; but the ...trange thing is that the hares actually seem ...o enjoy it. When the planes land and take off, ...he hares often race alongside as if trying to ...utstrip them. This reckless behaviour is in

line with the reputation brown hares have and it is hardly surprising therefore that such expressions as 'hare-brained' have come into being and are popularly used.

Although we now partially understand the brown hare's strange spring behaviour, there is still much that remains steeped in folklore. For instance there is an ancient belief in parts of Wales that the hare changes sex every month. Certainly distinguishing the two sexes is often difficult, but the best way to tell them apart is by watching the mating ritual – when they go 'hopping mad'. Perhaps it is not so surprising to learn that the word hare derives from the Anglo-Saxon 'hara' which means to jump.

The hare digs a narrow resting hollow or form, which it lies in during the day. The form is dug out slightly more at one end than the other – the deeper end accommodates the hare's large and powerful hind quarters. The form is usually orientated so that the hare can sit with its back against the wind.

RABBITS: FAST BREEDERS

Threatened by pest control, shotguns and the dreadful toll taken by the virus myxomatosis, rabbits still have an amazing ability to recover and survive in great numbers.

Rabbits were not known in the British Isles before about the 12th century. It is thought they were introduced then from the Continent to provide sport for noblemen and to provide a new source of food and fur. They were originally kept in fenced enclosures, but managed to escape and became the most successful colonizers of all time.

Rabbit spotting You will find rabbits living wherever grass grows, but they particularly favour areas of short grassland such as downland and closely-grazed agricultural land. Their ideal habitat is a small field bounded by hedgebanks, which provide cover and a refuge from predators, and they favour well-drained sandy soil which makes burrowing easy. Normally rabbits prefer to come out of their burrows at twilight and after dark; but if the area is quiet and undisturbed they will appear in broad daylight to feed. The months of May and June are a good time to go looking for rabbits; many you see then are likely to be youngsters. Rabbits do not hibernate in winter so you can still see them in cold weather, although they will be mostly mature adults.

Hopping gait The rabbit's Latin name– *Oryctolagus cuniculus*–means 'burrowing little hare', but in fact the rabbit and the hare are quite different. The rabbit is generally smaller and moves very differently, making it fairly simple to distinguish even at a distance. It hops along in a series of little leaps, one fore-

Above: A doe may produce over 20 kittens each year, in a succession of litters about every 30 days during the breeding season.

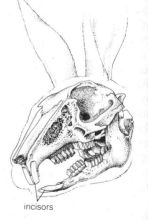

incisors

Above: Each large incisor at the front of the jaws is chisel-shaped, with a large cutting edge. Behind these are the cheek teeth.

Above: The courtship rituals are elaborate; here the doe accepts the advances of the buck. The young are born in the nest (right); these are 6 days old.

...w slightly ahead of the other, while the hare ...pes with long bounding strides. You cannot ...iss the flashing white underside of the ...bbit's tail (scut) when it is running at speed. ...s characteristic hopping gait with the bot-...m bobbing up and down is produced by the ...owerful, heavily-muscled hind legs which ...e much longer than the front ones. At high ...eeds the rabbit's hind legs land ahead of its ...orepaws. In muddy ground, snow or sand ...is leaves an easily recognisable track – two ...rge prints side by side in the front (made by ...e hind legs) and a small round print behind ...nade by the two forepaws closer together).

Furry animal Rabbit fur is soft, thick, ...ense and very variable in colour. You may ...e individuals with fur of any shade ranging ...etween greyish-brown and sandy-yellow; ...e nape of the neck is usually reddish while ...e flanks are buff and the underparts white ...r grey. The distinctive tail, white on the ...nderside, is brown or black on top. Young ...abbits sometimes have a white star on their ...orehead, but you hardly ever see this in ...dults. A few black (melanic) and some ...lbino rabbits do exist, the black being more ...ommon than the white. All rabbits moult ...eir fur once a year, usually in the period ...etween late July and September – the 'neu-...ral' season when neither mating nor breeding ... taking place.

Sensing predators The rabbit has superb ...quipment for detecting potential danger. Its ...ong sensitive ears can be turned in a variety ...f directions to catch the faintest sound, while ...ts large bulbous eyes are spaced wide apart ...nd angled on the sides of the head so it can ...ee in an arc of over 180 degrees. In addition ...he rabbit has an acute sense of smell assisted ...y two sensitive pads situated around the ...ostrils; these pads are covered by flaps of ...kin which can be retracted to increase ...ensitivity. You will often see a rabbit sitting ...pright on its hind legs turning its head this ...vay and that to catch scent, sight or sound of ...riend or foe.

Although its furry, soft shape and habit of ...unning away when disturbed may lead you ...o think the rabbit is timid, it can fight ...erociously when necessary and inflict serious ...njuries with its powerful kicking hind legs ...nd sharp claws. Also the first pair of incisors

(there are two pairs in the upper jaw, one small pair behind the big ones) are large and chisel-shaped with a sharp edge and can give a nasty bite.

Social order Although one rabbit may look very much like another, each one is an individual and has to find its own place in the rabbit hierarchy. At the top of the social ladder is the dominant buck who requires all rabbits of lesser status to move out of his way and vacate the best grazing land and burrows. Next in line are the older bucks and does who in turn dominate the weaker or younger rabbits. This system of dominance and sub-servience is usually called the pecking order – and it exists to a greater or lesser degree throughout the animal kingdom. It is par-ticularly important in animals which live together in large numbers, serving to establish order in a community.

Defending territory All rabbits establish strongly guarded territories which are sharply defined. The buck marks his territory by rub-bing his chin along the ground and secreting a strong-smelling, colourless substance from a gland beneath his jaw. An old buck's chin can become bare through constant 'chinning'. The doe also behaves in this way, but to a lesser degree since she is not so concerned with maintaining a territory. The dominant buck guards his territory using display and threat tactics designed to intimidate those of lesser rank. These tactics include squirting urine, scratching the ground with his forepaws, hopping towards other rabbits with a peculiar stiff-legged gait and grazing in short, sharp bites in the direction of the offending under-ling. If all these threats are ignored, the buck will attack.

Relationships Aggressive encounters are generally bloodless; if, however, threat and

RABBIT (*Oryctolagus cuniculus*)
Size of adult rarely exceeds 50cm (19in) and 2kg (4lb); female smaller.
Colour coat greyish-brown, underparts white or grey.
Breeding season one litter every 30 days from November to June.
Gestation period 28 days.
No of young 4-6, max 12.
Lifespan average 1-2 years, potential max 8-9 years.
Food grasses, cereal crops, tree bark.
Predators man; fox, stoat, weasel, badger, ferret; owls, hawks, eagles; wild and domestic cats, dogs.
Distribution grassland especially where hedges, woodland or scrub provide cover. Heaviest in south and south-east England.

Rabbit signs tracks smaller than hares' in print and hopping pattern (shown below). Droppings can be seen near the warren.

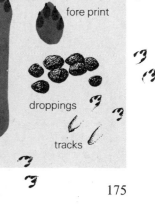

hind print

fore print

droppings

tracks

Life in the Warren

If you see rabbits feeding or hopping across a field, a warren is likely to be fairly near. Rabbits are social creatures and prefer to live together in groups. They dig burrows which form an extensive underground system of inter-connecting tunnels, nests, side galleries and entrance/exit holes. The entrance holes are usually about 15cm (6in) in diameter and the warren tunnels can reach as deep as 3m (10ft) below ground.

You should be able to spot the main entrance at once by the presence of rabbits (above), or by signs of extensive excavations, a mound of soil outside the hole and an area of sparse vegetation which has been worn down by constant passage.

Tufts of rabbit fur on snags in fences and hedges also indicate a warren nearby. Other signs are droppings and tracks. Warrens are situated where tree roots, tall plants such as ragwort and nettles, banks and hedgerows provide cover against predators.

Tunnel systems are constantly enlarged and the warren can undermine a whole system of fields. As rabbits often feed close to their burrows, they also produce a zone of sparse vegetation which may cause serious soil erosion.

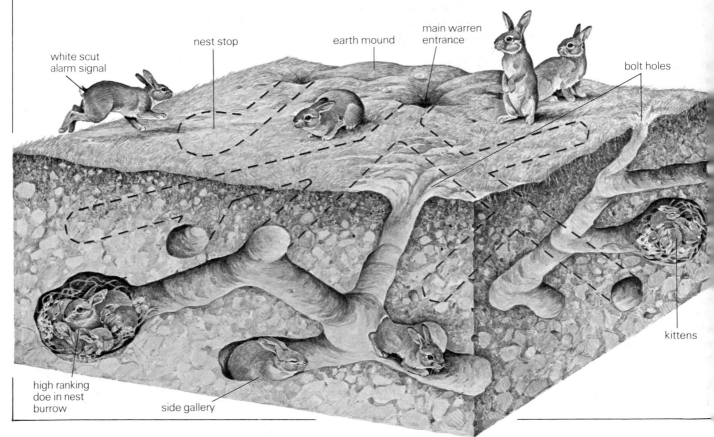

play fail to resolve a territorial conflict, ious conflict may ensue. Vicious battles olving much kicking, biting, tearing of fur d screaming have been known to occur tween rival bucks.

In courtship rabbits can display a more ntle nature. Sometimes buck and doe will side by side, or facing, and lick each other's ehead, ears and neck in a calm, relaxed nner; or they will play together at night, asing each other in small circles in a kind of ptial dance. Mating probably occurs inly in the burrows at night, when less sturbance is likely from predators or other bbits.

Home security In spring the pregnant doe rts digging her first burrow and sets up the me she and her young will need. The doe gs in very much the same way as a dog; she es her forepaws to excavate and throws ck most of the soil with her hind legs. The ck will assist with the digging but rarely ends more than a few minutes at it. Apart om feeding he is occupied with defending st and territory, and guarding the doe ainst other males.

Two types of burrow are prepared. Does of gher rank build their nests deep within the arren, inside one of the subterranean gal- ries. The younger, weaker does have to make special burrow—known as a nesting stop— vay from the main warren. The doe lines her urrow with scraps of straw, leaves and moss d also pulls fur from a pad on her chest to ake the lining even softer. She replaces cavated soil very carefully to make the nest trance inconspicuous and to deceive pos- ble predators. A chimney-like aperture is tained, leading to the surface so air can rculate freely and allow the kittens, when ey are born, to breathe.

Weaning young The new kittens, always orn at night, are helpless creatures—blind eaf and hairless and weighing a little over 0g (1½oz). The doe opens the nest for a short eriod at night to suckle her young and seals it p again when she leaves. Within seven days he weight of the kittens doubles, their fur rows and their teeth and claws become isible. They are suckled for up to a month. ince the doe can be pregnant again even only 2 hours after giving birth (and is nearly lways so by two days after), she must suckle nd wean her young as quickly as possible.

Population control A doe will produce oung only if the environmental conditions re favourable. She will conceive, but in imes of food shortage or really great over- rowding (or if there is a continual round of kirmishes and squabbles in the colony), she vill re-absorb the embryos completely. This xtraordinary form of birth control is more revalent among younger, weaker does.

Despite all precautions taken by the doe, oxes and badgers often find their way inside he burrows, scraping the soil away from bove or uncovering the main entrance. Bur-

rows built at a greater depth are less likely to be invaded by these larger predators, but are vulnerable to weasels and stoats who are small enough to get right inside the warren. In lowland areas, flooding can be another hazard and the young of dominant does living in deep warrens suffer most. It seems in these regions a balance is set up between the two types of burrow. If the weather is exception- ally wet, the young in the shallow nesting stops are more likely to survive; if there are many predators the young in deep burrows will probably fare better.

When a colony becomes overpopulated, the young rabbits in their first year must move out if they are to survive. They stray some- times far and wide during the autumn and early winter and may fall victim to pre- dators—of which there are a very large number. Foxes, stoats, weasels, badgers, owls, hawks, cats, dogs and even man himself all attack rabbits. If they survive this onslaught, however, they will set up more breeding colonies to threaten farmers and their pre- cious crops.

Above: This rabbit makes convenient use of a large stone for extra reach in getting food.

Killer virus
The virus myxomatosis arrived in England in 1953 via the bloodsucking rabbit flea attached to migratory birds, which had fed on the carcase of a diseased rabbit, or was secretly imported by farmers as a pest control. Symptoms are swellings of jelly-like material on the base of the ears, forehead, nose, anal and genital regions. The eyelids become thick and stick together. The inflamed areas finally exude a watery fluid and the rabbit dies—usually within 11 to 18 days. Rabbits may be growing immune, or the virus weakening, but it will probably never die out.

The mole surfacing from its burrow system shows its characteristic pink snout, surrounded by sensitive whiskers, and its rich black fur. This fur will lie either way so the mole can move forwards or backwards along a tunnel without jamming its hairs in the burrow wall.

THE UNDERGROUND LIFE OF THE MOLE

Moles are the most solitary of mammals, living in their own restricted system of underground tunnels for most of the year and usually ignoring each other. When they do meet, they fight until the weaker mole retreats. This is true of both sexes – the female is just as aggressive and quarrelsome.

The mole was living in Britain 7000 years ago when the land mass was finally separated from Europe – and from Ireland, which the mole never reached – after the last glacial period. At that time lowland Britain was mainly covered with deciduous forest, which was the natural habitat of the mole.

Today the mole is most commonly found in grassland and pasture – a fact largely borne out by the abundance of mole hills, consisting of the soil excavated when burrows are made. However the mole is still present – if harder to notice – in deciduous woods and forests. Here it has a network of semi-permanent tunnels, which may be used by successive generations over a period of many years. (The author has observed such burrows in constant use in an oak wood near his home for at least 20 years.)

Tunnel food-traps Each mole has its own territory, an area of perhaps 450 square metres (550sq yd), which contains the tunnels in which it lives. The total length of the burrow varies; but in clay, which has a rich supply of insects and worms, it may be be-

en 100 and 200 metres (300-650ft). This
derground system acts as a huge 'pitfall
p'; the mole feeds by running up and down
burrows picking up the worms, insects and
er invertebrates which fall down into it.

deciduous woodland and old pasture,
rms are the most important source of food,
t huge numbers of insects may also be
ten. One mole's stomach was found to
ntain nearly 1000 tiny ants.

Territory and numbers Where there is little
sturbance and plenty of soil fauna, par-
ularly in woodland, the tunnels are the
ortest and the most permanent. Here the
ole has little difficulty in finding enough
od. There are seldom more than six mole
ritories, each with a single mole occupant,
a couple of acres – an area which might also
pport some three tons of worms, which is
fficient food for a much larger population.
owever, moles also turn up in poor sandy
ils like the breckland of East Anglia. Here
e food is much less plentiful, and a much
nger tunnel system is needed. You will
erefore find many more mole hills but far
wer moles in such places.

Although the mole leads a solitary life,
ually within its limited territory, it also
ems to have a shared or communal tunnel
a main run – where it is possible to catch a
fferent mole every day for a week or more.
bservations suggest that some territories
ay be more attractive than others; when the
ole occupying the most desirable area is
moved, another will replace it – and then
self be caught.

Nests Every mole has one or more nests
onnecting with the tunnels. The nest is
sually the shape of a rugby ball, about 20cm
in) in length. It is lined with dry grass or
ead leaves. The mole surfaces to collect such
egetation, although whether more so in
aylight or at night time is debatable. It does
ome out of its burrow more frequently than
often realised, although it is hard to observe
ince it moves stealthily in long grass. In very
ry weather its tunnels may not produce
ufficient food, and this will encourage the
ole to seek prey elsewhere. As a rule a mole's
bove-ground foraging is only for a short
eriod; it soon disappears underground to its
riginal burrow. If there is not enough food,
mole may sometimes abandon one area
nd move on to set up home after travelling
or several hundred metres.

Mating, but not matey The cosy, friendly
nimal described so charmingly in *The Wind
n the Willows* is in stark contrast to the anti-
ocial and aggressive individual found in
ature. The only vestige of social life is seen
n early spring, when the sexes come together
riefly to mate. Normally, when a male mole
neets a female mole, they fight; however, in
February the male may leave his home bur-
ow and set out to find a female. Often when
e enters her burrow he is rudely repulsed.
Occasionally the female is receptive and

briefly accepts the attentions of the male; he,
in turn temporarily loses his aggressive
instincts. The animals only remain together
for a brief period, possibly a few hours, and
then the male departs, often returning to his
original territory. This might not appear a
very efficient way to ensure successful breeding, but in fact it is very rare to find a female
which is not pregnant by late spring.

Early life At birth the young are pink,
naked and helpless. They are suckled by their
mother for up to four weeks, during which
period they grow rapidly, develop their
characteristic fur and reach half their adult
weight. They soon begin to take solid food –
chewed-up worms brought by the mother –
and to explore the burrows near the nest.
After about six weeks they are able to support
themselves, and then the family breaks up for
good. The young and the mother have by now
become less tolerant of each other, and it
seems likely that the parent, becoming tired
by her maternal duties, drives her offspring
away when they can be expected to be able to
look after themselves.

For some weeks after leaving the mother,
young moles spend a lot of time moving
above ground. During this period many are
attacked by predators, especially birds of
prey, and during the early summer the pellets
of tawny owls frequently contain mole bones.
It is not uncommon either to find squashed
mole corpses on roads. Eventually, however,

Earthworms are the mole's
staple diet. Like insects,
they are usually caught
underground as they fall
through the soil into the
mole's tunnel. However,
since earthworms surface at
night, it seems likely that
moles come above ground
under cover of darkness to
catch them. This would also
suggest why moles
themselves often fall prey to
another nocturnal hunter,
the tawny owl.

Many mole hills do not always mean many moles. They may indicate that the soil is not rich in invertebrates, so the mole is forced to excavate more extensively to catch enough food.

the fortunate survivors resume a subterranean mode of life. Some, particularly in woodland, may be lucky enough to find an untenanted burrow which they take over. The others have to dig in for themselves.

Are moles blind? There is still a lot left to discover about moles–for example, whether or not they are blind. They do have eyes, with all the parts of the normal mammal eye –a lens, iris and a retina; but the optic nerve is poorly developed, with only a fraction of the number of nerve fibres found in, for instance, a mouse or a vole. Some experiments have suggested that moles do respond to light, but it can be argued that the reaction may be due to the nose detecting the heat of

the light source. If you move very slowly do not create noise and vibration, you shine a bright electric torch full in the face a captive animal and get no apparent reacti The mole behaves very differently, howe if you tap on the surface of the ground qu lightly. If it is eating a worm, it will stop, d its prey and retreat. It is interesting to n that the species of mole found in south Europe (*Talpa caeca*) has its eyes cove permanently with a flap of skin and is, as latin name implies, blind; probably our o mole is almost equally sightless.

Sensors The mole does have well develop senses, so that it is able to live under a w variety of conditions with evident success. hearing is effective if not particularly ac and its quite keen sense of smell can detec worm at a distance of several centimetres has sensitive bristles on its nose and oth parts of its body, but it is the naked, pig-li snout which is the mole's most importa sense organ. The snout is covered w thousands of minute raised bumps (papill; which are richly supplied with nerve endin; These receptors are known as Eimer's orga Their exact purpose and how they work h not been fully investigated, but they appear detect air movement and vibration. The m runs up and down its tunnel at a speed nearly three miles an hour, which for such small creature corresponds to that of a ca tering horse. It would clearly be painful if

Looking inside the fortress

The fortress is an extra large mole hill–up to 50cm (20in) high and one metre (40in) across–containing the nest in which the young are born. It is built by the female and no two fortresses are alike, since the number of internal burrows and their positioning vary. The numerous burrows may provide a choice of escape routes or may be necessary to give the nest good ventilation.

The nest, which usually contains young in April or May, is made from whatever dry leaves and grass are available above ground. The mother spends a lot of her time away from the nest feeding, returning to suckle the young only during her rest periods. If she is disturbed she may move her babies to another nest.

Some females don't build fortresses, but instead rear their young in the nest they have been living in during the winter. Why some moles build fortresses is still a mystery, although it may be that these above-ground structures give protection against flooding (fortresses do occur in marshy areas).

A fortress constructed on marshy ground.

The nest is made of grass and leaves.

There are usually several exit tunnels from a nest.

There are usually four baby moles. They are about 14 days old when their fur grows and about 22 days old when their eyes open. The young leave the nest after about five weeks.

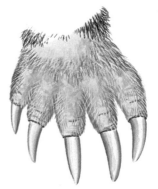

The mole digs through the soil by thrusting its forelimbs sideways and backwards in a breaststroke action. The close-up (above) reveals an almost circular hand with five large, strong claws—powerfully adapted for digging. The result of this digging activity can be seen by the opened mole fortress (left).

in its nose into the stony wall of the burrow.

Tracking moles Moles are active during the day and at night, and have a characteristic pattern of behaviour. This has been studied with captive moles, whose sleeping and feeding periods have been monitored. Moles have also been studied in the field, where rings of relatively harmless radioactive material have been attached around the base of the tail and the moles, moving underground, have been tracked from the surface with the use of a geiger counter (which detects radiation).

Three days in one Research has shown that the mole fits in three 'mole days' to our one—even though it is obviously dark all the time underground. The mole spends about four hours sleeping quietly in its nest; it then emerges and moves about its burrow for the next four hours: this makes up a mole's day—and it has three such periods every 24 hours. The mole's activity depends in fact on the food supply. If it finds a few large earthworms, it quickly fills its stomach and does not need to forage for more food. If food is very plentiful, it may collect extra worms, bite off their heads to prevent them burrowing away, and stack them in a small compartment off the side of the burrow, which acts as a larder—ready to supply food when fresh sources are scarce. If, after four hours searching, the mole has not filled its belly, it retires to sleep, so as not to waste energy, until more food falls

into the burrow system. If after several fruitless periods of searching it is still hungry, it will then either dig some further lengths of burrow in the hope that they will prove more productive, or even come out on the surface and, possibly, move to another location. On warm moist nights, when earthworms can be found on the surface of lawns, moles come out to catch them; and in very dry weather, when few worms enter the burrows, food–particularly a variety of insects–is sought above the ground.

Most moles, however, particularly in woodland, find an adequate food supply, and remain throughout the year in their own small restricted territories.

Diminutive mole To anyone whose only knowledge of a mole comes from the mole hills which appear in fields and gardens, the smallness of this mammal will probably come as a surprise if it is spotted or its corpse found. The mole's compact, cylindrical shape is well suited for moving up and down a burrow. Although it appears to have no neck, its bone structure here is similar to that of other mammals. It also has immensely powerful shoulders, which help the forelimbs to dig through the soil. Despite the fact that it spends so much time in the earth, it remains reasonably clean, even in muddy conditions. This is because its fur repels water. When the mole dies, its fur loses this water-resistance; corpses are invariably encrusted with dirt.

MOLE (*Talpa europaea*)
Also called mouldwarp or moldewarp ('earth-thrower')
Size of adult up to 15cm (6in) long, without tail; weight 80-150g (3-5oz); females slightly smaller
Colour black; orange rare
Breeding season young born March or April; one litter a year
Lifespan average 3 years for those surviving high mortality in first 3 months (few reliable records)
Food earthworms, insects; will eat carrion, or in captivity beefsteak and liver
Predators man, owls, weasels; domestic cats and dogs kill moles, but seldom eat them
Distribution in Britain, except peat bogs, mountains; no moles in Ireland or most Scottish islands

THE SOMNOLENT DORMOUSE

The tiny nocturnal dormouse is the only British rodent to hibernate, spending half the year asleep in a specially constructed winter nest. When awake it clambers with speed and agility among the branches of low growing shrubs searching for food.

The dormouse belongs to a family all of it own, the Gliridae, and not to the mous family which is the Muridae. Two species o dormice are found in Britain, the native common dormouse (*Muscardinus avellanarius* and the edible or fat dormouse (*Glis glis* which was introduced by Lord Rothschild ir 1902. The edible dormouse may have beer introduced previously by the Romans who considered it a gastronomic delight.

The common dormouse has acquired many descriptive local names. Hazel mouse refers to one of its favourite habitats and items of food—hazel bushes and hazel nuts. Dory mouse derives from the French verb *dormir* to sleep, and refers to the fact that the dor-

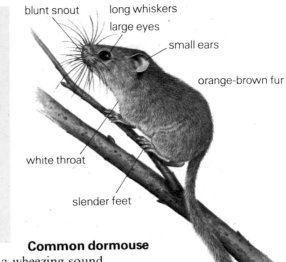

blunt snout
long whiskers
large eyes
small ears
orange-brown fur
white throat
slender feet
long bushy tail

Common dormouse

...ouse spends almost half the year hibernating in a torpid state. Another common ...me, the sleeper, also derives from its ...estyle.

Appearance The dormouse is a very small ...dent, the head and body together measuring ...ly 80-85mm (3-3½in) in length. It has a ...unt snout with long whiskers which may be ... to 30mm (1¼in) long. Its ears are small but ...ominent and it has the large eyes character-...ic of many nocturnal animals. Its unusual ...eek teeth, which have crosswise ridges on ...eir grinding surfaces, distinguish it from all ...her British rodents.

The fur of its upperparts is a rich orange-...own, fading gradually to a pale buff on its ...lly and pure white on its throat. Young ...ormice have greyer fur than the adults, and ...en among adults there is considerable ...ariation in coat colour. In October the ...ormouse moults to its winter coat.

The tail is 56-68mm (2¼-2½in) long, almost ...e same length as the body, and is the same ...olour as the upperparts. It is hairy, though ...ot as bushy as that of the edible dormouse.

The feet of the common dormouse, which ...re slender, adept at grasping and capable of ...reat 'wrist' and 'ankle' movement, enable it ... scamper with speed and agility along twigs ...nd thin branches.

Solitary, nocturnal and active The dor-...ouse is a solitary, nocturnal mammal, ...pending the day asleep and only emerging at ...usk to search for food. When awake it is ...ery active, moving with great speed and ...gility. Most small rodents spend their time ...earching for food on the ground, occasion-...lly going up into the branches of trees and ...ushes to look for buds or berries. The dor-...mouse, on the other hand, spends almost its ...ntire active life off the ground, among the ...ranches of bushes such as hazel. It scrambles ...igh up the branches of small trees, climbs ...imbly among the thin twigs and branches of ...ow shrubs and bushes, and scampers up and ...down the twining stems of brambles and ...oneysuckle. It is capable of leaping con-...iderable distances—a foot (30cm) or even ...more. All this frenetic activity is directed ...owards a single-minded search for food. ...During the five or six months of hibernation ...the dormouse loses a considerable propor-...tion of its body weight. All summer it feeds ...on the plentiful supplies of nuts, seeds, bark, ...fruit, acorns, haws, pine seeds, and young ...shoots, as well as on insects and snails. It is ...particularly fond of hazel nuts which are ...extremely fattening and therefore an ideal ...food as winter approaches. It does not crack ...the nut open but gnaws a very small, neat, ...round hole through which it extracts the ...kernel.

The common dormouse generally goes ...about its business quietly, although it has ...been heard to make shrill squeaking noises ...when chased. Mewing and purring sounds ...have also been recorded, and hibernating

COMMON DORMOUSE (*Muscardinus avellanarius*)
Size Head and body length 80-85mm (3-3½in), weight 23-43g (1-1½oz).
Colour Upperparts orange-brown, underparts pale buff, throat white.
Breeding season April-September.
Gestation 22-24 days.
No of young 1 or 2 litters per year, 3-5 young in each.
Food Mainly nuts, fruit and berries.
Distribution Mainly southern England, absent from Ireland and Scotland.

dormice sometimes make a wheezing sound.

Busy nest builder During the course of one year the dormouse makes two, or in the case of the female three, different types of nest.

The winter nest, in which it hibernates, is made of grass, dead leaves and moss and usually contains a store of food. It is built on the ground under a pile of dead leaves, or below the ground in the shelter of the roots of a small tree.

The summer nest is for sleeping in during the day. It is a loosely constructed ball of grass, leaves and shredded honeysuckle bark. It is usually about the size of a golf ball—just big enough to contain one dormouse.

The breeding nest is built in late spring in

Below: Areas with shrubby tree growth are the best places to look for signs of the common dormouse, especially where there are plants with edible seeds and an undergrowth of honeysuckle and bramble.

Above: The common dormouse is extremely lively and agile and adept at climbing among the thin twigs of low bushes and shrubs. Its feet are slender, and its flexible toes enable it to scramble about with ease.

Right: Hazel nut shells that have a smooth, neat, round hole in them have been opened by the common dormouse. Other rodents leave a more ragged hole.

readiness for the two litters of young. Th nest resembles the day nest but is mu larger, being over twice the diameter a more compactly constructed. It is usual sited near to the ground—much lower dov than the daytime nest.

Unlike the nests of birds, the dormouse nests do not have distinctive entrance hole Once inside its nest the dormouse closes t wall material behind it, making it impossib to see where it got into the nest. When startle it will break out from the nest at any poi and scurry away to safety. So if a dormou: nest has an obvious opening in it, you can t sure the owner is not in residence.

Breeding cycle The life cycle of the do mouse is not well documented and even th length and time of the breeding cycle is n definitely known. The gestation period between 22 to 24 days—fairly long for such small mammal. Two litters of between thre and five young are produced each summe Young dormice have been found in June so seems likely that mating takes place in Apr and May—soon after they come out c hibernation. Young dormice are also foun later in the season in August or early Se tember—and even in October. This suggest that the second mating occurs in summer.

The young are born blind and naked bu after 13 days their first grey coat is well grown By 18 days their eyes have opened and the have moulted into a paler version of th adult's orange coloured coat. They moul into their full adult coat at a year old. By 3 days old the young dormice are able t forage for themselves outside the breedin nest and by 40 days they are completel independent.

Young dormice do not become sexuall mature until the year following their birth During their first winter hibernation the weigh little more than half the adult weight

Life expectancy If it escapes predation the common dormouse can expect to live as long as four years, though six years have been recorded for dormice in captivity. This is a long life for a mammal of this size. The dor mouse is most vulnerable during the winter when it is hibernating. In its nest at ground level it falls easy prey to hungry magpies, crows, foxes, badgers, stoats and weasels. It is thought that four out of every five dormice die at this time of year.

Hibernation The dormouse is the only British rodent to hibernate. As winter ap proaches, it gorges itself and rapidly increases in weight. This excess fat is burned off slowly during the long winter sleep—during which time it may lose half its body weight. Dor mice usually hibernate alone although young dormice may occasionally hibernate together.

The winter nest is usually constructed in October. Each day the periods of sleep become longer and longer until the time comes when the dormouse does not wake at night to go foraging. From the end of

tober until the following April it remains
led up in a tight ball, its chin resting on its
ly, eyes and mouth tightly shut and its
curled over its head.

While it is in this comatose state, the
rmouse's bodily functions are maintained
a very low rate. In effect this little warm-
ooded animal becomes cold-blooded, with
art beat and breathing almost stopped and
dy temperature only a little more than its
rroundings (but never below freezing point).
e longest recorded period of hibernation is
months and twenty-three days.

In decline? In Victorian times dormice
re very common, and were even kept as
ts just as children today keep guinea pigs
hamsters. They are very even tempered and
not bite. This once abundant creature is
w quite scarce, for reasons that are not
lly understood. Loss of suitable habitat is
actor contributing to its decline. The wide-
read mechanisation of farming in this
ntury has caused habitats to be destroyed
an accelerating rate, and there has been
despread uprooting of hedges, a decline
coppicing and generally a loss of wood-
nd – all factors which affect dormice.

Today the dormouse can be found in
eatest abundance in the south of England.
the west, and north it is rare, in the Mid-
nds and East Anglia it is rare or totally
sent and it does not occur at all in Scotland,
eland and the Isle of Man.

Above: The young are born
blind and naked, but after
13 days their first grey coat
is well grown.

Below: A summer nest for
daytime roosting.

Where to look for nests

1 The summer daytime roosting nest is a
loose structure, usually wedged in the
fork of a tree and about 3m (10ft) above
the ground. It has no entrance hole.
2 The breeding nest is made by the
females in summer for rearing the young.
It is usually placed near the ground.
3 The winter nest, for hibernation, is
built on or below the ground, under
dead leaves or among tree roots.

ON THE FOX'S TRAIL

Most young dog foxes leave their parents' territory in autumn. By spring they should have found their own patch, but some become 'homeless' bachelor travellers.

As dawn breaks across a frosty hill-top, the countryside seems bleak and empty. But where the wind or sun has not removed the previous night's tracks, the whitish crust is broken by a line of prints—each one oval and each threaded to the next by a scuffed line, where a bushy tail has been dragged along.

The tracks are unmistakably those of a fox. Where the same trail is followed twice in heavy snow, the same footprints are used—an economical way of moving in otherwise tiring conditions. The criss-cross of tracks shows that by night both predator and prey were about, each set of tracks telling a story; how a vole dashed into a snowy tunnel as the fox dug frantically behind it; or how the

The fox is acutely aware of its surroundings: it has a strong sense of smell and its pointed ears are sensitive scanners. It is, however, unlikely to spot you if you keep perfectly still. The eyes are better adapted for night vision and nocturnal hunting

tackled a meal of a sheep's carcase. ...you learn to read the fox's tracks in snow, ...d or mud, you can begin to gather clues ...ut its night-time activities.

Population problems Winter time is a diffi-...t season for foxes. Growing cubs have ...her left their parents' home territory or are ...mpeting for a place in the community. ...her way, the population has been doubled ...even trebled by maturing youngsters. ...evitably many will have died by the spring ...the hands of man—mounted horsemen out ...nting, commercial trappers after pelts, ...mers worried about their livestock, game-...epers protecting their birds or local ...thority officials concerned about possible ...alth risks. Although in theory foxes could ...e as long as dogs—about 10 years—they ...rely do. The majority die before the end of ...e first winter and, in most places, few sur-...ve a third year. Where foxes are not ...rrassed by man, the population contains ...ore older animals and consequently a more ...ble society emerges.

The teeth of dead foxes obtained from ...nters in different parts of the world have ...en examined to find out their average age. ...e fox's tooth is treated with acid to remove ...e hard calcium. Thin sections of the tooth ...e then cut and stained for examination ...der the microscope. The stain reveals lines ...ound the tip of the root; these are annual ...owth rings, similar to those that signify the age of a tree or shell. These studies have confirmed that of the hunted animals, most were younger foxes.

Territories and travelling In winter the snowy tracks across the hill often reveal that the fox has travelled huge distances by night. Sometimes the tracks lead up hill and down dale in an unrelenting straight line; this probably indicates that the fox that made them was a maturing male, looking for a mate and territory of his own.

Most young dog (male) foxes seem to leave their parents' territory in autumn. Sometimes they do not leave immediately, but make ever more lengthy excursions into the neighbour-ing countryside. It is not clear whether the young foxes make these excursions–or even-tually depart altogether–because they are driven out by their father or because of some inborn urge to leave the territory in which they were born. Dog foxes normally travel farther from their birthplace than females do, so the risk of some possible inbreeding is reduced. Some vixens, perhaps many, do not disperse at all. Instead they remain in their parents' territory for their entire life.

Just how fox society works still provokes much debate. One thing, however, is certain: foxes are very flexible in their social ties. They can live successfully in many varied habitats by adapting to local conditions.

Members of the community usually fall into two types. The territory-holding animals

Contrary to popular belief, foxes are not totally solitary animals. Where they live in groups, they cohabit happily. These two young foxes indulge in mutual grooming.

live for long periods in the same patch and defend their borders from neighbouring foxes. The size of the territory can vary from as little as 25–50 acres to well over 250 acres. The resident foxes sometimes live in pairs, but a single dog fox can join with several vixens to form a larger group when food is plentiful and harassment by man is infrequent. Much of the evidence suggests that such cohabiting vixens are close relatives, perhaps mother and daughter or sisters. At night these foxes cover almost exactly the same area and their routes often overlap, depending on the local food supply. The foxes, however, travel independently and not in packs.

Where the habitat provides enough food and shelter for foxes, it is more likely that a young vixen in her first winter will be able to stay at home. If an elder sister or her mother dies in the autumn, the youngster can fill the vacancy in the group. By doing so she avoids all the risks of travelling across unknown country in search of a vacant territory—and perhaps not even finding a vacancy.

The second type of fox involves the more foot-loose itinerants (usually young dogs) who do not seem to have a patch of their own and who travel relatively large distances. Not only do they trespass on the territories of resident foxes, but they are often also the victims of the huntsman and his hounds because they are travelling across unfamiliar territory. Traps and snares can also catch them unawares. Little is known about these travelling foxes because they are so hard to study—even with the most sophisticated techniques such as radio-tracking.

Fox-talk Foxes have a wide vocabulary of noises and each call can be made with a variety of pitches. A night spent in a woodland in winter listening to dramatic fox choruses will convince any sceptic that foxes have a complicated system of communication. Foxes make noises throughout the year, but reach their peak in mid-winter.

Each call probably serves several functions. It may enable the caller to identify itself and its position, or communicate with other members of the caller's group—its neighbours and rivals, offspring and mates. There are

four recognisable types of fox calls. Perhaps the one most frequently heard is the 'wow-wow-wow' call, the repeated syllables of which trail eerily into the night, often to be answered by another fox. On some occasions, when this call fluctuates, the fox is clearly moving.

A second type of call is the screech—often known as the vixen's scream, although dog foxes also make this noise. Many countrymen believe vixens make this call when they are on heat to attract males. But it still remains a mystery and a frequent source of alarmed telephone calls to the police from householders who fear some hideous crime is being committed in their back garden.

The fox is a most adaptable and enterprising British mammal; few other species would probably follow this fox as it walks gingerly over the ice. The tracks and brush line left along the ice and surrounding frost would be clear evidence that a fox had passed through this area.

Finding foxes

Although they cloak their movements in darkness, foxes leave plenty of signs for the sleuth.

Smell The most obvious is the rather acrid smell of urine which occasionally hangs above a woodland path or glade and can normally be traced to a tussock of vegetation, which may be topped with fresh droppings. These droppings are generally left on top of open sites, as they are part of the fox's scent-marking vocabulary. They can be distinguished from those of dogs by the rather sweeter smell, the obvious presence of bone chips,

insect shells, traces of fur and feather and sometimes by curly pointed ends.

Footprints can best be followed in snow. The edges of puddles or ditches, however, can also yield clues. The fox's footprint is oval, about 6cm (2in) long and 4cm (1½in) wide (depending on the softness of the mud); dog tracks are rounder. The two front claws of the forefeet normally leave pin-prick impressions close together, where dogs' claws would be more spread out. The tracks of some dogs, particularly sheepdogs, can be very fox-like. A trotting fox travels in a straight line and in snow leaves tracks stretching out like a necklace.

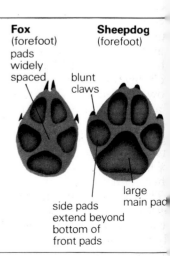

Fox (forefoot) pads widely spaced

Sheepdog (forefoot)

blunt claws

side pads extend beyond bottom of front pads

large main pad

The geography of a fox territory

A family group of foxes will confine most of its hunting activity to its home territory —which in this illustration is an area of farmland with plentiful food supply. During the night foxes may travel many miles criss-crossing their home range in search of food. The size of this area and the size of the group will vary depending on the amount of food available.

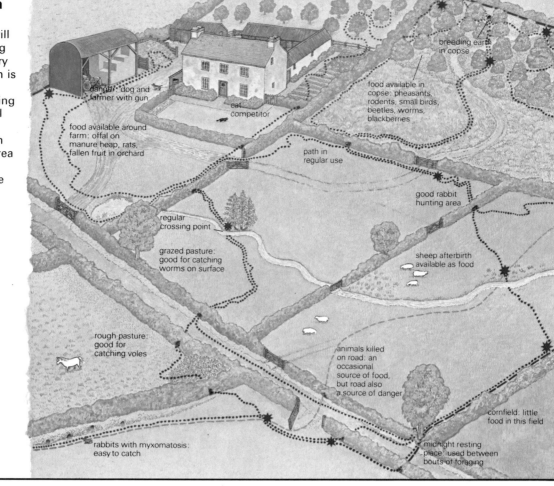

Key

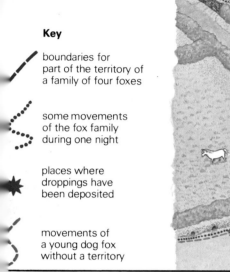

boundaries for part of the territory of a family of four foxes

some movements of the fox family during one night

places where droppings have been deposited

movements of a young dog fox without a territory

To hear the other types of fox noise, the eavesdropper needs to be close at hand, since the noises are made when foxes are in contact. One is called gekkering, a mechanical staccato noise which sounds similar to the clicking noise made by a football supporter's rattle. This noise is sometimes called clicketting and the word may also be used to describe the foxes' mating season, when squabbles involving gekkering can be heard. Often interspersed with gekkering is a collection of whines and whimpers which can be heard when foxes greet each other, or when dominant foxes bully subordinate ones. Foxes almost never growl and, unlike the stuffed specimens in glass cases, they never snarl.

Scent and sex Another form of communication between foxes—scent marking—is also best seen in the winter's snow. If you follow a set of tracks across the snow, it probably won't be long before you find a snow-covered tussock or mole-hill with signs of a sprinkling of urine. Both vixens and dog foxes go in for this sort of lamp-post annointing, just like male dogs. You can follow two sets of fox tracks and find that each time one fox has made a mark with urine, so has the other.

These tracks mirror the behaviour of a courting pair, with the dog fox marking over the scent of his vixen. When the two eventually mate they will lock together like dogs for up to half an hour. The vixen is only receptive for three or four days a year and so during that period the dog fox follows her incessantly. Once they have mated, contact between the two becomes less frequent until spring when the business of cub-rearing begins. At this stage the dog fox must find enough food to satisfy the hunger not only of himself but also of the vixen and the cubs.

Because few people have been able to watch foxes mating, little is known about the behaviour involved. Some have stumbled over a mating pair which were alone in the woods, while others claim to have seen a vixen followed by several males, sometimes a line of them following her scent. One suggestion is that the vixen will mate with only one dog, while another theory is that several dogs will mount her.

Much remains to be learnt about the role of the male in fox society, and this applies also to the travelling male. To understand what the travelling fox is up to necessitates knowing not only about its family circumstances 'at home', but also about all the foxes it meets as it travels—and, most important of all, the foxes in the place where it eventually settles. Does it, for example, have to find a territory where one male has died, thus leaving a vacancy, or can it oust a weaker or ageing male? The resources and manpower required to answer such questions are so great that the bachelor fox's secrets are secure for the time being.

FOX (*Vulpes vulpes*) also called Reynard
Size Dog (male) head and body 67cm (25in), tail 38cm (15in), weight 6.7kg (14lb). Vixen (female) slightly smaller and less heavy
Colour rusty brown to red above, dark grey to white below. Back of ears and points of limbs dark or black. Tip of tail may be white, but presence or absence is no indication of age or sex. Variously prominent dark face markings may be present. Overall 'speckling' from black/yellow/brown guard hairs.
Breeding season Late January. Cubs born in late March, but this varies up to a month before and after
Gestation period 52 days
Number of young 1-10, with an average of 4-5
Lifespan 2-3 years, with maximum around 10 years
Food Hares, rabbits, mice, voles, small birds, fruit, insects, earthworms, carrion
Predators man—farmers, sportsmen, gamekeepers, trappers, local government officials concerned with foxes as disease-carrying pests
Distribution throughout mainland Britain (not in some islands like the Hebrides)

INDEX

The entries listed in **bold** type refer to main subjects. The page numbers in *italics* indicate illustrations. Medium type entries refer to the text.

INDEX

ACKNOWLEDGEMENTS

Photographers' credits: A-Z Collection 16, 59(bottom), 63, 65, 74: Heather Angel 9(middle, bottom), 12, 26(bottom left), 30-31, 32(top, middle), 36(bottom), 37, 39(top), 42(top), 43(middle), 46, 47, 49, 51(middle), 53(middle), 61, 62, 64(top, middle), 70, 71(top), 72, 77(bottom), 79, 81, 82(middle), 83, 88(top), 91, 114(middle), 121(middle), 122(bottom), 123(middle), 138(bottom), 148(middle), 180(top), 182: Aquila Photographics/EA Janes 148(top); M&V Lane 19; J Roberts 59(top); MC Wilkes 134(bottom): Ian Beames 22(lower middle), 148(bottom), 161, 174, 186: FV Blackburn 126: Bob Gibbons Photography/B Gibbons 27, 38(middle, bottom), 115(middle), 159(bottom): Bruce Coleman Ltd/J Burton 118(top), 122(top), 169(bottom), 175, 178, 179; J Markham 163; D Middleton 173(top); H Reinhard 130, 136, 138(top), 154-5, 156, 159(bottom), 160, 162(bottom), 170: M Chinery 13, 34: W Condry 51(bottom): A Davies 18(bottom), 177: D Green 29, 139(bottom), 140(bottom), 141, 153: M Grey 139(top): B Hawkes 60, 98, 128: Harry Smith Collection 92(bottom): E&D Hosking/S Beaufoy 22(upper middle): GE Hyde 35, 53(bottom), 67(middle), 83, 95, 102(bottom), 116: EA Janes 54: G Kerby 8(bottom): M King & M Read/G Dore 44-5, 56, 92(middle): G Kinns 43(bottom), 165: M Leach 176: D Macdonald 187: S&O Mathews 6-7: John Mason 40(bottom), 43(top), 58(top), 78, 109, 112: Richard

Mills 94, 132(bottom), 134(middle): Colin Molyneux 41: Pat Morris 14(bottom), 21, 118(bottom), 157, 162(bottom), 180(top): NHPA/J&M Bain 73; J&M Bain & G Cambridge 50(bottom), 66; A Barnes 152; J Blossom 171, 181; N Brown 100(bottom); AA Butcher 92(top); A Callow 167; DN Dalton 36(middle), 146, 149; S Dalton 11(top), 114(middle), 167, 168; R&C Foord 77(top); JB Free 117; J Good 132(top); B Hawkes 22(bottom), 67(bottom), 82(bottom), 84, 133, 135(top), 147, 188; EA Janes 30(bottom), 50(top), 52, 96-7, 101(middle), 102(middle), 145(top); J Jeffery 144; WJC Murray 17, 135(bottom), 145(middle), 173(bottom); KG Preston-Mafham 55(middle), 110; M Savonius 55(bottom), 57; J Sauvanet 90(top); MWF Tweedie 107(top): Nature Photographers Ltd/SC Bisserot 123(bottom); FV Blackburn 24(bottom), 58(bottom), 125-6, 143, 151; B Burbidge 113(bottom); AA Butcher 25(bottom); K Carlson 142(bottom); A Cleave 8(top), 14(top), 15, 71(bottom); DMT Etlinger 88(bottom); J Hyett 75(top left); M Leach 11(bottom); O Newman 9(top), 28(bottom), 183, 184(top), 185; T Schilling 75(top right); D Sewell 137; P Sterry 10, 36(top), 39(bottom), 111, 115(top); R Tidman 23; JB Wilson 89: Naturfoto/K Holgard 106; Jacana 127; Schmidt 172: JF Preedy 158: Premaphotos Wildlife/KG Preston-Mafham 24-5(top), 26(bottom right), 64(bottom), 80, 82(top), 90(bottom), 101(top), 105(top), 119(top), 120, 121(top): Press-tige Pictures/D Avon & T Tilford 140(top),

142(top), 166; T Tilford 169(top): Richard Revels 28(top), 33, 103, 104, 105(bottom), 107(bottom): John Robinson 18(top), 22(top), 32(bottom), 48, 99, 113(top), 131, 164, 184(bottom): D Sewell 38(top), 42(bottom): Susan Griggs Agency/A Woolfitt front cover: BS Turner 129: MWF Tweedie 119(bottom): UNHA/P Morrison 150: G Wilkinson 55(top): T Wood 68-9.
Artists' credits: Graham Allen/Linden Artists 158, 161, 167, 168, 169, 183: Norman Arlott 127, 131, 144, 145, 181: Rhoda Burns/Drawing Attention 13: Sarah De Ath/Linden Artists 45: Wayne Ford 125, 134, 137, 141, 147, 149, 152, 153: Angus Gray-Burbridge/The Garden Studio 35: Hayward Art Group 20, 69, 71, 73, 74, 75, 76, 77, 84, 85, 86, 87, 108, 109, 130, 153, 171, 172, 174, 175, 176, 180, 188: Kristin Jacob 91: Felicity Kayes/The Garden Studio 116, 117: Richard Lewington/The Garden Studio 97, 98, 99, 100, 101, 104, 105, 111, 112(upper), 114, 115, 119, 121: Andy Martin 189: David More/Linden Artists 47, 48, 51, 53, 55, 58, 59, 61, 67, 94, 95: Paul Nesbitt 87(top): Sandra Pond 27(line): Gordon Riley 123: Nina Roberts/The Garden Studio 185: Colin Salmon 10(original research Gillian Kerby), 112(adapted from DR Rage 1964), 139, 141(map): Joan Sellwood/The Garden Studio 3, 155, 164: Helen Senior/Groom & Pickerill 81: Carole Vincer 79: Phil Weare/Linden Artists 26, 27.

Index compiled by Richard Raper of Indexing Specialists, Hove, East Sussex.

Typesetting GRANGE FILMSETTING LTD. BIRMINGHAM; Printing HUNTERPRINT GROUP PLC; Separations YORK HOUSE GRAPHICS, HANWELL; COLOURSCAN OVERSEAS CO PTE LTD. SINGAPORE; Binding HAZELL WATSON & VINEY LTD. AYLESBURY.